With Compliments

Best wishes,

Clare Ellis

THE LAND
of the
KOMODO DRAGON

© 1998 Times Editions Pte Ltd

Published by Times Editions Pte Ltd
Times Centre
1 New Industrial Road
Singapore 536196
Fax: (65) 2854871
Tel: (65) 2848844
e-mail: te@corp.tpl.com.sg

Times Subang
Lot 46, Subang Hi-Tech Industrial Park
Batu Tiga
40000 Shah Alam
Selangor Darul Ehsan
Malaysia
Fax & Tel: (603) 7363517

Printed in Singapore

ISBN 981 204 765 4

THE LAND
of the
KOMODO DRAGON

CLAIRE ELLIS

TIMES EDITIONS

Contents

Introduction

In Indonesia the Komodo dragon is known as the *ora, biawak Komodo, buaya darat* (land crocodile) or *mbou*. These names are perhaps more precise than the name of the group of lizards the animal belongs to, the monitor lizards. Monitor lizards were first observed by Europeans in North Africa, where the Arabic word for the common species, the Nile Monitor, was *ouran,* which sounded like *waran* to the Germans. This became confused with the English 'warn' and German *warnen* (meaning 'to warn'). So the animal became a 'warning lizard', and later its name was altered to 'monitor', giving rise to the myth that it warned man of the presence of crocodiles.

The distortion of facts seems to have followed the Komodo dragon. Until recently little was known about the animal, and scientists made assumptions based on the few field studies done and information gathered about other monitor lizards and reptiles. The inaccuracies were compounded by travel writers looking for a good story but finding facts hard to come by. Figures and stories have been handed down with little checking on the reality behind them, creating considerable misconceptions. It is hoped that this book will help correct some of them.

As most of the Komodo dragons live in Komodo National Park, this book focuses largely on this area.

Place Names

Place spellings differ from map to map. Most are phonetically based on the local languages and then altered slightly when incorporated into Indonesian. For instance, the large bay in front of Kampung Komodo is Soq Lawi in local Komodo, or Teluk Slawi or Loh Lawi in Indonesian.

If one understands a little of the original language, some of the place names in the book start to make sense. Below are some words used for geographic features in the local Komodo language, Indonesian and English.

Komodo language	Indonesian	English
banu	*air, sungai, mata air*	water
soq	*teluk, loh*	bay
ntodo	*gunung*	mount
nusa	*pulau, gili*	island

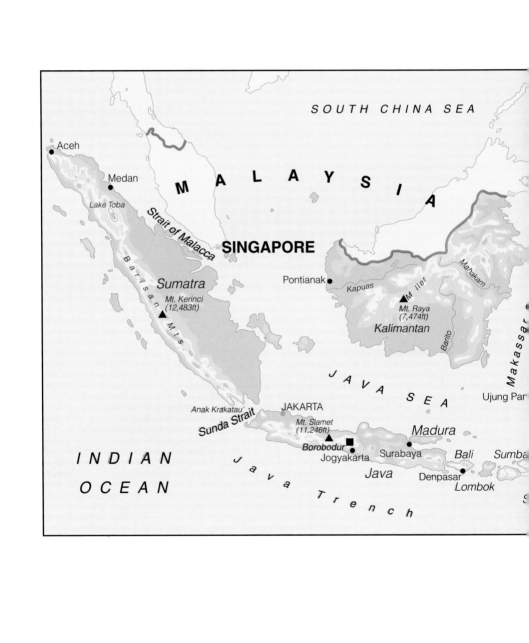

INDONESIA

N

LAWESI SEA

Manado •

Moluccas

Sulawesi

Irian Jaya

▲
Mt. Jaya
(16,499ft)

PAPUA NEW GUINEA

BANDA SEA

odo Island

Flores Trench

Flores

• Ende

Timor

ARAFURA SEA

The Komodo Region

Location

About 450 km east of Bali, at 8–9°S, 119–120°E, is a cluster of tiny islands. Lying between Sumbawa and Flores Islands, these, and scattered locales on Flores, are the only homes of the Komodo dragon. A national park now straddles some of this area.

Left: Much of Padar is covered with grass, so Gunung Pyramide's striking shape stands out.

Geography

Steep hills, rocky ground, shallow soil, long droughts and regular fires on these relatively small islands

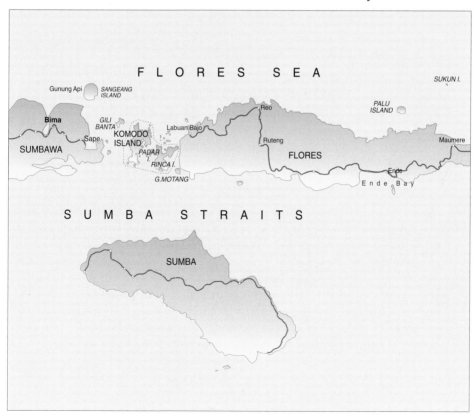

11

Distribution of Komodo Dragons

Area	Size (km²)	Estimated no. of Komodo dragons*	Geographical features
Komodo Island	339	1,600	Gunung Satalibo, 738 m, Gunung Ara, 823 m, Gunung Komodo, 655 m, Doro Otota, 518 m
Padar Island	20	-	Gunung Pyramide, 269 m, and an unnamed peak at 279 m
Rinca Island	198	1,100	Doro Ora, 667 m
Gili Motang	33	70	Central peak 441 m
Wai Wuul Reserve	30	100	Inland, low hills
Mbeliling and Nggorang Reserve	310	Few	Low hills

* Estimates from the park authority (1994 statistics)

mean the vegetation is sparse and the animals few. These harsh, rugged island habitats of the Komodo dragon have helped shape the animal through its evolutionary history. As the largest predator in the region, the animal fills the top ecological niche on the islands. It is hard to imagine a creature better adapted to its environment than this opportunistic scavenger and hunter, which can go for weeks without fresh water.

Each island, separated from its neighbours by dangerous swirling currents, has its own characteristics, as do the reserves on Flores.

Komodo Island

Like its namesake the Komodo dragon, Komodo Island dominates the region. It is the largest and rockiest island, with forest-covered, well-worn peaks running down its length. The tallest, Gunung (Mount) Ara, is sometimes incorrectly called Gunung Arab—after an unverified story about Arab settlers.

The south of the island is wetter than the north, but few streams flow all year round. Many last only a couple of days after the rains stop. However, during the wet season fresh water pools can be found at higher elevations. Enlarged by pigs and water buffalo, some are 1 m deep and 25 m in diameter, and last all year round.

The lack of water has helped limit human settlement, and the island has only one village, Kampung Komodo. Two kilometres away is the principal ranger station, Loh Liang. From here numerous tracks head into the wilderness, allowing visitors to admire the flora, fauna and magnificent panorama of the island. Several other ranger stations have also been established, but they are used mainly by anti-poaching patrols and for combating fire rather than for facilitating tourism.

Padar Island

Long and thin, with relatively little tree cover, Padar Island receives the lowest rainfall in the area. The island's minimal forest cover means that many of the larger animals are not found on it. Nor is the impressive lontar palm. Three fresh water sources seep out from the base of the hills. Although the island is uninhabited (and always has been, apart from a Komodo National Park post that lasted a few years), local fishermen claim the water is some of the cleanest in the park. Rocky headlands are interspersed by sandy beaches, valuable as turtle nesting sites.

Possibly due to the limited availability of food, the density of Komodo dragons was always low and their physical size small on Padar. Some time after 1970 they disappeared from the island, but a small population may now have returned.

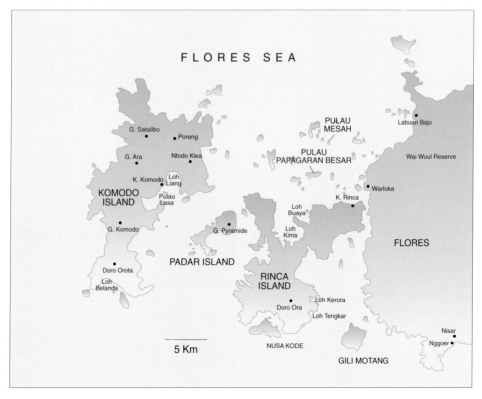

Plants make the most of the scarce rain and burst forth with leaves and flowers, such as this member of the legume family common near the beaches.

Rinca Island

Rinca is also spelt Rindja, Rintja and Rinja, but the pronunciation remains unchanged as *Reen-cha*. As on Komodo, limited fresh water has restricted the growth of villages and agriculture. Rinca has only two villages—Kampung Rinca and Kampung Kerora. There were others in the east, but they are now used only as seasonal camps. Pearls are cultured in two locations, and there is a ranger station open to visitors at Loh Buaya. The island is the only one in the region with cacti, wild horses and monkeys. It has good scenery and plentiful wildlife, including Komodos, and is rapidly developing as a tourist destination.

Gili Motang

Rarely visited, the small, round island of Gili Motang is flanked by majestic rock formations. It appears to have a small permanent Komodo dragon population, although some scientists suggest that the Komodos seen may be only visitors.

Flores

In contrast to the other islands, Flores is enormous (360 km by 70 km). About 1.8 million inhabitants cling to its rugged volcanic slopes. Despite its size, it has limited Komodo dragon habitat—the animals dislike the cooler, higher areas, preferring the coastal strip where grassland and forest meet.

The exact distribution of Komodo dragons on Flores is not known, but the population is shrinking as habitats become increasingly fragmented due to human encroachment. Two reserves have been established on the west coast of Flores— Wai Wuul/Mburak (also spelt Wae Wuul) and Mbeliling and Nggorang. Both are managed for purposes of scientific research and conservation, unlike Komodo National Park, which takes into consideration tourism and the lives of local villagers. As there may be slight but significant genetic differences between the Komodo dragons here and on Komodo Island, these reserves are very important for the animal's survival.

Labuan Bajo, a picturesque fishing village with a population of about 4,000, is the site of the Komodo National Park headquarters. The town has accommodation, travel companies and an airport, and is a key entry point to the park.

Other Islands

Nusa Kode (9.6 km²) or Oewada Sami, off Rinca, is believed to be the smallest island with a permanent population of Komodos, but no conclusive studies have been done to find out whether they breed there.

Outside the park boundaries is Gili Banta. Volcanic in origin, it has no Komodo dragons, but it has excellent diving and snorkelling sites, and there are moves to include it within the park.

Countless other tiny islets and reefs make navigation a hazard even

Temperatures rise dramatically during the day, and virtually every animal rests.

Rocky outcrops and convoluted coastlines create impressive scenery.

for locals. Most are scattered on the northeastern side of Komodo and to the north and east above Rinca. Much of the area is designated as the park's buffer zone. Despite the lack of fresh water there are major villages on the islands of Papagaran Besar and Pulau Mesah.

Climate

The savannah of Komodo stands in striking contrast to the tropical rain forest covering much of Indonesia. Komodo is one of the driest areas in the archipelago. Hot, dry winds from central Australia blow in a northwesterly direction for most of the year, and only from late December to March do the rain-bearing northwest monsoon clouds

reach the island. Even then, the rains are sparse: in a good year they may amount to only 800 mm, with the average being around 650 mm. Most plants and animals, including the Komodo dragon, take advantage of the bounty of the rainy season and reproduce around this time. The rest of the year, plants must survive on dew and the odd shower.

The annual average temperature at sea level is around 27°C, but there is significant variation through the year. When the wet season ends, temperatures start climbing and day temperatures reach 40 to 43°C. Humidity drops to a low of about 75 percent in October. At the height of the rains, usually in February, temperatures are at their lowest but the humidity is higher.

These figures are deceptive, as they describe the general climatic conditions faced by the visitor rather than the micro-climate in which the Komodo dragon lives. Hatchlings live in trees, but for the adult Komodo, a cold-blooded reptile that must actively regulate its body temperature, the temperature at or near ground level is crucial. At ground level there is little wind and greater radiation, and temperatures can rise significantly higher than the air temperature. Overheating and dehydration are serious issues for all the flora and fauna of the area.

Geology

Jagged, fanglike peaks jut wildly into the sky, while other hilltops appear worn, rounded and smooth, giving a hint of the Komodo area's complex geological history. Indonesia lies on an explosive mix of moving tectonic plates and has more active volcanoes than any other country. Earthquakes are a daily event in one part of the archipelago or another. The islands lie on four plates—the Indian-Australian, the Pacific, the Eurasian and the Philippine—which are moving all the time. The Indian-Australian plate is pushing northwards, and its forces are still creating and shaping the chain of islands running from Sumatra down through Java and Bali and on to Nusa Tenggara (where Komodo Island lies).

The Komodo region is typified by intense geological activity, with volcanism, tectonic movement and sea level changes. As a result, the islands consist mostly of fine-grained igneous rock from volcanic activity. Coralline limestone formed in shallow water has also been uplifted to create land.

Until recently the islands were thought to have been formed no earlier than the Plio-Pleistocene period. As the Komodo dragon is believed to have evolved before this, in the Pliocene period (4 to 5 million years ago), there is great debate over the animal's origins. However, recent geological work suggests that parts of Komodo Island were formed in the Jurassic period and that inhabitable land surfaces in the region may have existed before the Pliocene period but did not correspond to the present-day shapes and sizes of Komodo, Padar, Rinca and Flores. Most geologists agree that the islands are likely to have been connected during certain recent periods, facilitating plant and animal migrations. Importantly for Komodo dragon distribution, Sumbawa does not appear to have ever been joined to these islands.

Despite localised uplift movements, for about the last 20,000 years the available land mass for the Komodo dragon has been contracting. A rising sea level has halved the Komodo's habitat and increased the distances between islands. While the Komodo can swim reasonably well, these larger distances may now be impassable barriers, limiting the movement of animals, and hence genes, between some of the island populations.

Unlike on the larger islands of Sumbawa and Flores, there are no active volcanoes in Komodo National Park. This does not mean that the area has remained

island group, but there appear to be no commercially valuable deposits.

Since it was declared a national park in 1980 the Komodo area has had rapidly increasing numbers of visitors.

The Discovery of the Islands and the Komodo Dragons

Bronze and iron implements reveal that man inhabited the Indonesian archipelago by 2500 B.C. However, evidence of occupation goes back much further than this; skulls of *Homo erectus* and early hominids have been found in Java, dating back perhaps 1.5 million years. Scientists disagree on the exact dates of the finds, but most do agree that neither developed here to become modern man, *Homo sapiens*.

The islands' enormous agricultural and natural wealth meant that populations could grow and cities flourish. Mighty empires rose and fell. The trade potential drew ships from as far afield as China, Arabia and India. Much later, in the 1500s, the Europeans discovered the routes to the Far East and the world opened up. These were great voyages of discovery, but the men were not exploring for the sake of exploration. They sought items that could be resold at vastly inflated prices back home. Huge profits justified the yearlong trips and great perils associated with them. Most of the explorers travelled to tiny islands in the Moluccas, known as the Spice Islands, the world's only source of mace, nutmeg and cloves, but some of them sailed to Nusa Tenggara (known earlier as the Lesser Sunda Islands) for turtle shell, sandalwood and pearls.

unaffected by recent volcanism. Tremors are frequently felt, usually originating off Flores. There are cataclysms too. On January 4, 1969, Kali Bara, Flores (about 300 km away from Komodo), erupted. A fine cloud blew northwestwards, covering parts of the islands in centimetre-thick dust. This killed new grasses and choked fresh water sources. Herbivores suffered, and there were reports of deer stumbling around. Adult Komodos no doubt benefited from this surplus of easy prey, but it must have been a difficult time for younger ones, whose normal food of insects would have been depleted.

Searches for mineral wealth have been conducted sporadically on the

Key points were identified on sailors' maps, but the tiny islands between Flores and Sumbawa remained an unvisited mystery. They had no large populations of restless natives requiring subduing, nor did they have spices or any other obvious items of value.

Surrounded by wild, swirling waters—which swept away unwary boats but brought a constant supply of fresh food and life-giving oxygen to the marine organisms—the area was always treated with respect and given a wide berth by sea captains. Yet the hidden riches of Komodo tempted the brave. A dazzling display of corals and invertebrate life meets the eye of today's recreational divers, but it was the fishermen and pearl divers who first understood and sought out Komodo Island.

As early as the second century A.D., Chinese traders were coming to Komodo seeking its underwater treasure trove of pearls. They returned home with tales that are said to have enhanced the mythology of the Chinese dragon, which had the same huge claws, forked tongue, reptilian scaly body and long, lashing tail of the Komodo dragon. Maps were made with a simple note—"Here be dragons"—warning people of the island's inhospitable nature. Komodo stories brought back by traders and fishermen were taken as the ravings of men who had been at sea too long. No one seriously thought dragons existed. Yet strange tales continued to filter out of ports.

Finally, a scientific expedition went out to settle the matter. A Dutch military officer stationed on Flores, Lieutenant van Steyn van Hensbroek, reached the island in

1911, shot an animal and sent the skin to the Zoological Museum at Bogor (then called Buitenzorg), Java. In 1912, after receiving a few more specimens, the museum's curator, Major P.A. Ouwens, properly identified the Komodo dragon as a member of the monitor lizard family and the largest lizard in the world.

Word spread quickly through the scientific community. A Dutch expedition killed another animal and sent the skull and skin to Leiden University in the Netherlands. World War I caused a lull in research, but after that it was not long before hunters and scientists returned to the Komodo area.

The public became aware of the animal after the visit of Douglas Burden, trustee of the American Museum of Natural History and world-renowned big game hunter. In 1926 his group visited Komodo Island and captured 19 Komodos. Two live animals were displayed at Bronx Zoo, New York, and 12 dead specimens were taken for study. Cameramen accompanied the group, and a short documentary was made and shown in cinemas. This, together with magazine articles, brought the islands into the international spotlight.

Scientific work on the population, distribution and behaviour patterns of the Komodo dragon trickled in. The most thorough work done to date is by Dr. Walter Auffenberg, a herpetologist from the University of Florida. Most of his pioneering research was done in 1969–73, and his subsequent publications are still considered the

History of Komodo Dragon Protection

Date	Regulation/event	Influence
Soon after 1912, probably in 1915	Sultan of Bima declared the animal protected.	Valid only within Sultanate borders
1926, ratified in 1930 by Resident of Timor	Decree of the Manggarai Regency (eastern Flores)	Prohibited capturing & killing of Komodos & possession of live or dead specimens, or parts thereof. Prohibited collection of eggs & disturbance of nests.
1931	Regulation for the Protection of Wild Animals declared; included Komodo dragon.	Countrywide
1938	South & west of Rinca & all of Padar declared game reserve.	First habitat protection
1965	Komodo Island included in reserve.	
1969	Wai Wuul Reserve established in west Flores.	
1970	Game reserve office established at Labuan Bajo.	Increased protection
1977	Listed with UNESCO as Man and Biosphere Area.	One of first four listed in Indonesia
1978	Indonesia signed Convention for International Trade in Endangered Species (CITES).	Komodo dragon listed in Appendix 1, meaning it cannot be transported internationally without proper paperwork & approval, nor can it be commercially traded.

Date	Regulation/event	Influence
1980	Komodo National Park established; dedicated by President Soeharto in 1988.	One of first five national parks declared in Indonesia
1984	Park boundaries extended seaward.	
1991	Designated as World Heritage Site by UNESCO.	One of only two natural sites listed in Indonesia
1992	Komodo National Wildlife Reserve Decree passed.	
–	Komodo dragon listed as 'Rare' by World Conservation Monitoring Center.	Not considered endangered, but because it lives in such a small geographic region, it is classified as 'at risk'.

primary texts for study. Continuing work has been done by various institutions and individuals, particularly within Indonesia by Putra Sastrawan and his students from the Udayana University in Bali.

Komodo National Park, its large marine areas, plus Wai Wuul Reserve and Mbeliling and Nggorang Reserve in west Flores, are managed by the National Park Authority (PHPA). The protected area totals almost 220,000 ha— almost four times the size of Manhattan Island.

This sounds impressive, but the logistics of providing real protection in an isolated area have been difficult. Poaching was extensive, according to reports from early visitors. Skins were collected. Chinese traders took hundreds of specimens for 'swimming med-icine', and animals' tails were used for 'burn medicine'. By 1972 per-haps 500 animals had been taken for zoos and scientific studies. The animals continue to be captured, with another 10 taken from Flores for Ragunan Zoo, Jakarta, in 1996.

While the park was formed mainly for the protection of the Komodo dragon, it also conserves some of the least disturbed re-maining dry lowland forests in the region and protects some of the country's best coral reefs. Current and future issues for the park and the Komodos, including the impact of tourism, are outlined in the chapter on conservation (page 81).

The Life of the Komodo Dragon

Information on the biology of Komodo dragons is still incomplete, and much work needs to be done. Few extensive field studies exist; Auffenberg's work of the early 1970s still stands as the most authoritative work available. Advances in scientific equipment—radio tracking devices, internal sensors, DNA blood tests and portable X-ray machines—mean more information can be obtained now than was earlier possible. Future studies may prove some current estimates and theories but refute others.

Opposite: This young Komodo dragon is almost too large to continue living in trees and will soon have to take its chances on the ground.

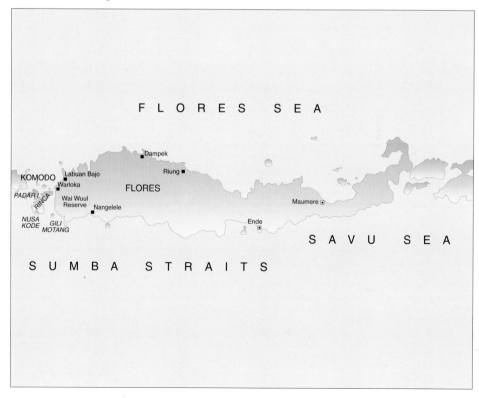

Basic Komodo Dragon Facts

- Scientifically, the Komodo dragon is known as *Varanus komodoensis*.
- It is the largest lizard in the world in terms of overall size (weight).
- Currently, about 3,000 are thought to live in the wild.
- The creature is found only on Komodo, its surrounding islands and a few isolated pockets of Flores Island.
- Totally carnivorous, it both scavenges and actively hunts.
- The largest specimen was recorded at the St. Louis Zoo in 1933. 'Minnie, the Dragon Lady', incorrectly named as it was a male, was 10 feet 2.5 inches (3.13 m) long. Stories of larger animals exist but cannot be proven.
- Weight varies depending on when the animal last ate, but the hunting weight of a very large Komodo dragon may be 250 kg.
- On average, a fully grown female may be about 1.8 m long and a male about 2.1 m.
- The Komodo dragon does not have any poison, but it does have various strains of bacteria in its saliva that infect a bitten animal.
- Like most predators it has good hearing and binocular vision, but its keenest sense is that of smell.
- It lives a mostly solitary life, either within a permanent home area (resident) or as a wanderer (transient).
- A very fast mover over short distances, the Komodo can run

The Komodo dragon is the largest lizard known in respect to size and weight.

Significant Events in the Komodo Dragon's Evolution

Geologic period (millions of years ago)	Occurrence	Time of occurrence (millions of years ago)
Triassic, 245–208	Age of Reptiles	245
Jurassic, 208–144	First lizards emerged.	200
Cretaceous, 144–66	Sub-family Varaninae emerged.	100
Tertiary: Paleocene, 66–57	Most of the Varaninae became extinct.	60
Tertiary: Miocene, 24–5.3	Present-day *Varanus* genera emerged in Asia.	15
Tertiary: Pliocene, 5.3–1.6	*Megalania prisca* emerged?	?
Tertiary: Pliocene, 5.3–1.6	Komodo dragon emerged?	4–5
Quaternary: Pleistocene 1.6–.01	*Megalania prisca* became extinct.	.01–.02

at 14 to 18 km/h although 8 to 10 km/h is more usual.

- The animal can swim well, frequently staying well below the surface, but it is not as strong a swimmer as some other members of the monitor lizard family.
- Babies live in trees for the first few years, partly to escape the cannibalistic adults, which are too heavy to climb trees.
- There appear to be slight colour variations between the adult Komodo dragon populations of Rinca and Flores (brick red) and those of Komodo Island (grey to black).

While impressive statistics of the Komodo dragon are tossed about, some care is needed in properly describing the animal. It is the largest lizard known in respect to overall size and weight, but it is not the longest. That distinction goes to the *Varanus salvadorii*, a 4.75 m long swamp dweller in Irian Jaya. But the bulk of the latter animal's length (70 percent) is made up of a thin, whiplike tail that helps it balance in trees, so it is nowhere near as heavy as a Komodo dragon.

Compared with other reptiles, the Komodo dragon is not unusually large. The longest snake is the reticulated python, which is 10 to 12 m long. The saltwater crocodile reaches 8.5 to 9 m, while the marine turtle takes the prize for heaviest reptile, with a leatherback turtle weighing up to 600 kg.

Ancestry

Theoretical studies on island biogeography have helped shed light on the evolutionary process known as giganticism. But the Komodo dragon still intrigues scientists as there appears to be no obvious explanation why this huge species of lizard emerged to live on only a few remote islands in eastern Indonesia.

As mentioned earlier, Komodo dragons belong to the monitor lizard family, powerful reptiles with well-developed limbs, eyes with moveable lids, small scales on the tops of their heads and deeply forked tongues. Spreading from west Africa through southeast Asia to the Philippines, and from as far north as the Caucasus to southern Australia (excluding Tasmania), monitors are a widely distributed family. Generally believed to have evolved on the supercontinent of Laurasia (North America and Eurasia), they appear to survive best where they do not have to compete against large mammalian carnivores. Monitor lizards are well adapted to arid zones, and the majority of the world's species now live in Australia.

The Komodo dragon's exact evolution is still debated, but a relatively recent ancestor is thought to be the 7 m long *Megalania prisca*. Known as the giant goanna, this magnificent carnivore was about 10 times as heavy as the present-day Komodo. Scientific reconstructions picture it to be very similar to today's Komodo dragon, a scavenger and hunter preying on large marsupial herbivores up to the size of the present-day hippopotamus, such as the diprotodon. The *Megalania prisca* lived throughout much of eastern Australia until 10,000 years ago but appears to have died out with the large marsupials as Australia became increasingly dry.

Perhaps evolving from early members of the giant goanna, the Komodo dragon emerged in the Pliocene period (4 to 5 million years ago), possibly feeding on stegadons (pygmy elephants about the size of present-day water buffalo) that roamed eastern Indonesia. Except for some fossils of disputed origin found in Timor and on Java, no bones or fossils have been found of the Komodo dragon to prove it lived elsewhere, and Auffenberg suggests that "a succession of land surfaces have been available in the Komodo area of the archipelago since its [the Komodo's] earliest development phase." As the Komodo dragon is able to swim, successive generations could migrate from subsiding to emerging islands. Auffenberg goes on to state, "it is very likely that the present distribution of *V. komodoensis* is at, or near, its geographical point of origin."

Present Distribution

The Komodo dragon has the smallest range of any of the world's large carnivores. Even so, its distribution is not precisely known. The Komodo dragon lives in a very narrow ecological band between the forest and savannah. Here, there is both sun and shade for thermoregulation and usually a high prey

Babies spend their first few years in trees.

density. Disliking wetter habitats, the animal exists only in dry areas and needs warm temperatures. The 500 m altitude mark is generally the habitat limit, although transients have been recorded much higher.

Komodo dragons are today found on the islands of Komodo, Rinca, Gili Motang and Nusa Kode (although there is some doubt whether the last two smaller islands support permanent populations). There were some on Padar until about 1970, but they disappeared—mainly due to deer poaching. A proposal to reintroduce Komodo dragons on Padar has been discussed, but it appears they may have returned naturally. In mid-1996 villagers spoke of having spotted the tracks of several Komodo dragons on the island. Whether this is a small breeding population or short-term visitors making the most of the currently abundant food is still to be determined. The animals also visit other small islands in the group, tempted by the smell of food. No confirmed reports have been made on Sumbawa, and the Sape Strait appears to act as a barrier to their westward movement. However, there is anecdotal evidence of an occasional crossing.

In Komodo National Park the animals' range and density is studied by rangers, but information on their distribution on Flores is much more scattered. Here the Komodos live in two major areas: along the south coast as far east as Nangelele and continuing along the western edge of the island (except in the populated area around Labuan Bajo); and on the north coast of Flores from near Dampek to just west of Riung. In each case the range is discontinuous and the Komodo dragon density is low, being broken by agriculture, protruding hills and generally unsuitable habitat.

There have been persistent rumours of Komodos existing in additional areas, although no conclusive studies have been done. Unlike at Banu Nggulung on Komodo Island, where the Komodo dragons have become used to man, wild Komodos are difficult to observe. On Flores they avoid populated areas, not just because the prey density is lower (man also hunts deer) but also because, despite their being protected animals, villagers have been known to poison or kill Komodo dragons that interfere with stock or attack people. Hence, the animals tend to live in remote areas. They are believed to live east of Riung, west of Maumere and just north of Ende. Additional work is needed to determine the location and extent of each population group on Flores, and the establishment of additional protected areas may be necessary. There are also occasional rumours of the creatures living in south-eastern Sumbawa, although this is highly unlikely.

Komodos are good swimmers, and it is surmised that they occasionally swim between some of these segregated populations, allowing genetic mixing of the population. However, the rising sea level has increased the distances between islands, and ripping currents make even short water crossings hazardous. In addition, man has isolated the Flores population of Komodo dragons. Thus, there is limited mixing of genes, and the groups on different islands may be slightly different from one another. An examination of the extent of genetic variability is currently being undertaken.

So How Many Komodo Dragons Are There?

Different methodologies give population numbers varying from 1,000 to 5,700. Auffenberg's well-accepted studies in the early 1970s resulted in some of the highest figures: 5,700 scavenging-age Komodos, with an estimated 1,500 babies born each year. Since then their numbers on Flores have declined, and there are probably very few, if any, permanently on Padar. 1994 estimates by park rangers are about 3,000 Komodos in total: 1,600 on Komodo Island, 1,100 on Rinca, 70 on Gili Motang and 100 at Wai Wuul. Numbers in the isolated pockets of Flores are thought to be very low.

With better controls, particularly over deer poaching, it will be interesting to see if these figures start to rise again. As the Komodo dragon's rate of replacement or life span in the wild is still unknown, its chances of long-term survival remain uncertain.

Home Range

Komodo dragons live a solitary life, either as wanderers or within a fixed home range. The young start as transients, travelling until they can find a home range, but some adults appear never to settle. The size of each animal's area depends mostly on food availability and may be up to 500 ha. It overlaps with other Komodos' areas. A small inner core area is crucial and must contain basking areas, shade zones and burrow sites. Often the core area also contains water holes and trails, giving the Komodo ambush sites. A Komodo dragon may travel up to 10 km per day but normally averages 1.8 km per day, regularly moving through the whole range, checking both for prey and for other Komodos.

The life of the transients is not well understood, and the extent to which they manage to breed successfully is not known. They may play an important role in population dynamics and gene movement.

Social Interactions

Although Komodo dragons are predominantly solitary, social status is quickly established when they gather in groups. When several of them are attracted to a carcass, the smaller ones are wary of the large males, who demand priority over the food. Chemical signals, often gathered from sniffing the droppings of other Komodos as they patrol, probably allow individual animals to recognise each other and are important in determining some behavioural patterns and mating. Visual signals are principally used

Loose wrinkles in the neck and belly region allow the skin to stretch when the animal eats large amounts of food.

around a carcass. If presence alone is insufficient to scare away a contender, an aggressive posture is adopted. Visual threats include lowering the head, holding it at an angle, arching and enlarging the neck, and arching the back and tail. A throaty, hissing sound may accompany this threat. If the animal is moving, the gait becomes slow and stiff legged. If this is insufficient, the tail may be lashed at the opponent. Actual attacks can lead to serious wounds or death.

During the courtship/mating period, closely matched males rear up on their hind legs and crash together like two sumo wrestlers to establish dominance. A lucky loser manages to run away, but a less fortunate one stays motionless as the victor sprawls on top, clawing its sides.

Eating Habits

Meals are irregular, so the Komodo must eat as much as possible when it finds food. More importantly, it needs to eat what it finds before other, perhaps larger, members of its kin smell and reach the same food source. Therefore, the animal has evolved in such a way that it can eat large quantities very quickly.

The Komodo dragon can eat up to 80 percent of its starved body weight in one sitting, which explains why quoted weights differ so much. For instance, a 50 kg animal was recorded eating a 31 kg pig in 17 minutes. To eat like this, a *National Geographic World* article nicely illustrated, a 60 lb (27 kg)

Deer form an important food source for adult Komodo dragons.

person would have to eat 200 quarter-pound burgers!

The Komodo does not chew its food or use its tongue while eating. Lumps of food are torn off, thrown to the back of the mouth and swallowed whole. Huge quantities of saliva help the chunks slide down. The prey may be smashed on the ground, both to kill a still-live animal and to help break it up. The Komodo may then use its wide, splayed front claws to hold down the carcass, creating extra leverage. Fur, bones and hoofs are all swallowed, as are deer antlers if they are still small. The head, thorax and front legs of a young goat may disappear in one bite. To get its mouth around this quantity, the Komodo has a highly developed level of cranial kinesis—moveable joints in the skull and jaw.

About 60 small (2 cm long), sharp, recurved, laterally compressed and serrated teeth line the mouth. In other words, they point backwards, cut very effectively and are designed to slice and tear, not chew. This tooth shape is rare in lizards but common in sharks. Yet compared to a crocodile or alligator, a Komodo dragon's gape seems quite innocuous. There is no sinister, toothy smile, as the tiny weapons are hidden in the fleshy gums.

Because of its irregular eating habits it is very difficult to say exactly how much a Komodo dragon eats. Captive Komodos are fed approximately 3 kg per week, meaning an adult would consume 156 kg per year. Compare this to a wolf—another top-level carnivore, about half the weight of an adult Komodo—which consumes approximately 1,277 kg of meat per year. This demonstrates the astounding survival efficiency of the Komodo dragon in its harsh environment. Of course, captive animals do not need to walk long distances to find food and may be away from their natural climatic habitats. But considering captive Komodos have problems with obesity, it is still an indicator.

Part of the reason they need less food is that they eat virtually all of the animal, usually leaving only the herbivorous stomach and intestine contents. They also digest more of every meal. Only 8 to 13 percent of the carcass is undigested, and therefore excreted, by a Komodo dragon, whereas this figure may be 32 to 37 percent in the case of a tiger.

This efficient digestive system is an adaptation to the dry conditions the Komodos live in. Rarely do they need to drink, as 85 percent of the liquid they need comes from their prey. When they do drink, it tends to be in significant quantities, such as after a very heavy meal to aid digestion. Very little fluid is excreted. From this and other data, it would appear that a wild Komodo dragon eats very well about once per month but eats a few small titbits between these larger irregular meals. After gorging, the animal sleeps. But it is not quite that simple. The Komodo must be careful to keep its body temperature relatively high to aid digestion. An elevated body temperature accelerates enzymatic action and mechanical digestion. Too slow a digestion process, at low body temperatures, may allow the food in the stomach to rot, causing the animal to regurgitate the food; this sometimes ends in death.

What Do They Eat?

Komodo dragons are purely carnivorous. They principally scavenge and sniff the wind to locate dead or dying animals. They have been observed eating everything from a dead dolphin washed up on the beach to leftover meat in a garbage dump. Rotting goat, the favourite bait of early travellers and film crews, was used to attract the predators in front of the cameras. It is not known whether the Komodo dragon actually prefers rotting flesh, or whether it is drawn by an old carcass because it smells stronger than a fresh one.

Scavenging generally takes less energy than hunting, so it tends to be the preferred method if sufficient food is available. But Komodo dragons are also active hunters. Eggs, birds, snakes, rodents, insects and other lizards are food for smaller Komodos, while larger ones eat goats, pigs, deer, even horses and water buffalo. Always liking an easy target, Komodos follow a pregnant animal soon to give birth. Seeing a Komodo near a female horse or goat, waiting to snatch the newborn and afterbirth as they reach the ground, is a grisly reminder of the animal's opportunistic eating habits. The weakened mother is also at risk if she does not move away in time.

While Komodo dragons are fast, they cannot chase down a deer or other swift-footed animal and instead ambush their prey. Rapidly dehydrated by the heat, most animals must regularly visit freshwater holes. It is along these game paths that Komodos plan their attack, in what is sometimes called the 'lurk 'n' lurch' approach. They lie motionless, well camouflaged, and are rarely seen until it is too late. When tackling large prey, they tend to seize the leg, tearing the hamstring, and then tear the throat and belly. With smaller prey they go straight for the throat or belly.

The Komodo is not always immediately successful in bringing down a large animal, but a bitten animal usually dies soon—although not from poison, as was earlier thought. Komodo dragon saliva is a haven for at least four types of toxic bacteria. Bacteria from the last rotting carcass that it fed on stay alive in the Komodo's mouth. Komodos frequently bite through their own gums as they eat, and the saliva-blood combination provides an ideal culture for the bacteria. The bitten animal is infected and suffers septicaemia, and the Komodo tracks the weakened animal using its superb sense of smell, harassing the prey until it eventually becomes a meal.

Curiously, the Komodo's large food sources—deer, horses, buffalo, pigs and goats—are all thought to have been introduced by man to the islands. It was common for sailors in past centuries to release live animals on islands, so that when they returned, perhaps after a long sea voyage, there would be a supply of tasty food available. So what did

The nine inch long forked tongue provides the Komodo dragon with a keen sense of smell.

the Komodo eat prior to this? If only smaller prey existed on the islands, why is the Komodo dragon so large? Evolution generally creates a predator no larger than needed to successfully hunt its prey.

In the early and mid-Pleistocene period (up to half a million years ago) two species of stegadons were known to exist on Flores. They would have provided plenty of food for the Komodo's large bulk. The time gap (if one existed) between the extinction of these animals and man's possible introduction of animals on the islands is hotly debated, but recent archaeological work suggests a much earlier presence of man in the Australasian area than was previously thought— thus, larger prey may have been available through most of the species' existence.

Smell

A Komodo dragon has nostrils, called nares, near the tip of its snout. These go back into the skull, where there is a pair of Jacobson's organs, the chemical analysis receptors. These organs are also connected to the roof of the mouth, so when the Komodo flicks its tongue in and out, it is sniffing the wind. Just like snakes, the Komodo has a long, narrow tongue that can protrude a good distance so as to sample a greater volume of air and thus collect more scent. Its tongue is a much better source of vital information than its nostrils, and so a Komodo swings its head from side to side as it flicks out its tongue.

The Komodos at Banu Nggulung have long been used to the clicking of tourist cameras and ignore their presence.

The different amounts of scent received from the two tongue tips allow it to determine the direction of the food source. It can then follow the scent trail to a carcass or wounded animal. When it arrives at the food source, it does not eat until it has touched the potential food with its tongue.

To get an idea of how keen this sense is, Auffenberg documented a Komodo dragon smelling a carcass 11 kilometres away, following the scent and finding the food. Of course this distance was dependent on the wind direction and strength, and on local topography, but it explains why a favourite resting place for Komodo dragons is on a hilltop facing the sea. These are not just good sun basking spots, but the sea breeze carries the scents up from the valleys below.

Hearing

Although early naturalists assumed they were deaf, Komodo dragons in fact have good hearing. Lady Broughton (1936) stated, "I discharged a shotgun over their heads at a range of a dozen yards on more than one occasion. Neither this nor the rattling of plateholders nor the human voice seemed to make any impression on them." Yet she goes on to say, "It is interesting to note that the specimens at the zoo very definitely hear the sound of the key turning in the lock of their cage." A Komodo dragon

Opposite: Burrows are dug in dry riverbanks or, as here in the foreground, on the hillside.

quickly turns its head to focus on rustling leaves in the undergrowth that may signal a meal, yet it will completely ignore tourists clapping their hands and shouting "hey you" to get a reaction for their cameras. The animals are simply selective in what they respond to. Knowing this, a number of tour operators at Loh Liang have perfected the noise of a goat bleating to encourage movement in the Komodo dragons!

Thermoregulation

The Komodo dragon, like all reptiles, must heat up its body by basking in the sun or on warm surfaces and cool it down in the shade or on moist surfaces. This is called thermoregulation: regulating the body temperature.

The resting body temperature is lower than the body temperature required to be active, and so, as the sun rises, the Komodo dragon moves from its burrow to bask in the sun, warming itself before it sets off to hunt. Midday it retreats into a burrow or the shade to stay cool. As temperatures drop again, it hunts before retiring for the night.

Burrows provide cool refuges in the daytime and warm homes at night. They also help the Komodo preserve water, as they provide a moister environment than the outside. The Komodo's strong front feet can dig a metre-deep hole in an hour, and the dens are usually about 1.5 m in length. Favourite sites are on the banks of dry creek beds or on open hillsides. The animal enters headfirst and then often curls back on itself, leaving both the head and tip of the tail at the entrance.

Because of the requirements of thermoregulation, most scientists agree that the Komodo dragon tends to sleep at night. In fact, a number of people claim that a Komodo is completely torpid at night and can be easily approached and examined. However, this is not true. Personal nocturnal observations of Komodos at Ragunan Zoo and in the wild on Komodo Island reveal they can be very active indeed!

Mating

The Komodo's mating habits are not yet fully understood. Much is surmised from a few brief sightings in the wild or observations around Banu Nggulung, where the animal's behaviour has probably been modified. Recent captive breeding work done by US zoos has enhanced knowledge in areas such as egg incubation temperatures, but there is still much to be done.

As mentioned earlier, the Komodo is normally solitary and territorial. Copulation often occurs after two animals have been attracted to the same carcass. In many animal species a ritualised courtship display is performed. This can serve two purposes. Not only does it signify the intentions of the male and sometimes help induce the female to ovulate, but it is used by many animals to determine the mate that may be able to pass on the strongest genes to the next generation. For some lizard species, typical body motions include head bobbing, dancing and hand waving. This type of behaviour has not been observed with Komodo dragons.

A male must completely subdue a female before attempting to mate with her.

Minimal or no pre-mating rituals are quite unusual for large animals capable of inflicting serious wounds on each other. Through the rest of the year aggression dominates. Males, being slightly larger, often drive off a female from a food source. So how does the female know that the male's advances are for mating and that she is not about to be attacked?

Some scientists theorise that the Komodo's acute sense of smell picks up the other's pheromones and so each animal already understands the other's intentions. It is also possible that individual animals already recognise each other and may have mated in previous years. Animals with overlapping ter-ritories are likely to have come across one another regularly, and some scientists have suggested long-term pair bonding may occur. If the same male and female mate each year, there may be no need for them to go through an extensive courtship display.

Long-term pair bonding has not been proven, however, and even if it did exist, it does not explain the situation of the free-ranging Komodos, who would not already have an association with another animal, nor the lack of courtship behaviour observed with young Komodos still presumably looking for a lifelong partner. Recent work suggests that polyandry, where the female accepts several males, and / or polygyny, where the male mates with more than one female in a season, are far more likely.

The mating season is in the middle of the year, around May to July. Occasionally, large, evenly matched male Komodos can be seen engaged in combat over a female. Rearing up onto their hind legs, they wrestle each other with their weight and front legs. They bite each other, and the sound of the undergrowth being trampled is drowned out by their angry hisses and the clash of their rough, scaly skins.

An unsuitable candidate is driven off by the female and may be bitten by her if he is not careful. The accepted male spends a great deal of time rapidly flicking his tongue around the female's face and on her sides just in front of her hind legs, presumably establishing that she is ready to mate. Mating is short and quick. The male wraps his tail around and below the female's and moves her tail to the side so he can reach her vent.

Determining Sex

Males grow much larger than females. A large Komodo, 2.5 to 3 m long and weighing perhaps 90 kg, is definitely a male, but it is hard to determine the sex of a smaller animal. Mature males have two internal lateral bulges at the base of their tails, called hemi-penes (between the fifth and sixth caudal vertebrae), so the male Komodo can mount the female and access her from either the right or the left side, but these are not evident from external examination. To complicate matters, females have elongated eversible sacs, which may be mistaken for the male sex organs.

Everything from colour differences to variations in nose shape, checking of cloacal rosettes and manual probing has been tried to distinguish the sexes, but these techniques are now considered unreliable. For years dissection was the only definitive method—not exactly conducive to breeding! Young Komodos can be sexed by gently manipulating the area around the cloaca, which causes the hemi-penes to emerge if they are present. This technique is not foolproof, nor can it be used on older animals.

While humans and other species have distinct chromosomal differences between males and females, the identification of sex by this technique for Komodos and some other reptiles is not straightforward. Different techniques for sexing the animals are being tested, such as X-ray, ultrasound, laparoscopy and trans-intestinal sonography, as well as blood, albumen and faecal hormone analysis, but some of these are obviously not possible in the field. This problem has caused scientists, zookeepers and rangers much confusion and despair. Pairs of Komodo dragons caught for zoos may turn out years later to be of the same sex.

Auffenberg, using the presence of cloacal rosettes on males, estimated that there were 3.4 males to every female in the wild. More males than females have been captured, supporting the suggestion of an uneven population ratio. Yet, females may simply be warier of baited traps, or because the males are more active and have bigger territories they may be more likely to be captured. It is crucial to know the sex ratio in the wild if more accurate population breeding estimates are to be made.

Life Cycle

Komodos have an annual reproductive cycle. One to two months (40 to 50 days) after mating, in July to September, the female digs a hole and lays her eggs. Two types of sites are favoured: on hillsides, where she often tunnels under a boulder; or in the huge nest sites of rotten vegetation and sand built by the orange-legged scrub fowl (see page 57). Disused nests, which no longer generate internal heat, are

This specimen, safely immobilised, is ready to have its blood sample and measurements taken.

preferred. The Komodo lays her eggs much deeper than the bird does—about 1.5 to 1.65 m below the surface—as Komodo eggs require incubation temperatures of 27.5 to 29°C. The birds need 32 to 34°C. Several test holes are often dug. Some collapse during the tunnelling, while others may be too damp, too dry or at the wrong temperature.

Compared to snakes and turtles, lizards lay few eggs. Komodos lay an average of 20 to 25 soft, leathery eggs each season, which constitute up to 20 percent of the female's normal body weight. The eggs are about twice the size of a chicken's (55 x 85 mm), weighing on average about 125 grams (captive-laid eggs are often heavier, 155 to 180 grams). Probably a quarter to a fifth of each

Wild Komodos are hard to spot and harder to approach.

clutch fails to hatch. Whole clutches may be eaten by predators, and so an estimated 25 percent of each season's eggs actually hatch.

Parental care after egg laying is minimal or nonexistent, yet some females stay around a nest site for weeks, aggressively defending it. Initially it was hypothesised that they waited until the smell of their digging and the scent of the eggs no longer remained fresh in the soil— if other Komodos, snakes, dogs, civet cats or even pigs smell the nest, they dig it up and eat the eggs. However, at least in some cases, it appears that the female is guarding the site prior to egg laying, perhaps protecting it from other females until she is ready to lay her own eggs. After that, she is weak and easily driven off by another female eager to use the site. The answer to this mystery may be that while some females lay their entire clutch over a few hours, in some cases egg laying is sporadic and takes several weeks. The nest defending behaviour may be associated with the slower egg laying.

The eggs must stay underground undetected for 8 to 9 months (200 to 250 days). All varanid eggs are very rich in lipids (fats), and the young embryos feed on the eggs before hatching towards the end of the rainy season, March to May. The hatchlings weigh approximately 70 to 100 grams at birth and are on average 30 to 40 cm long.

Unlike their parents, young Komodos are attractive—with yellow spots and stripes, fine, pointy faces and long, thin bodies.

Their colouring provides camouflage against their many predators. Under 1 m long, they are vulnerable to attack from rats, dogs, civet cats, snakes and birds of prey, as well as other Komodos. The tail forms a much greater percentage of the body length in young Komodos than it does in adults, an adaptation to the former's tree-living years. This allows them to avoid ground predators and stops them from competing for the same scarce food resources as adults. Newborns feed on lizards, especially geckos, baby birds and insects, all of which are abundant for a few months after the rains. Rodents and birds form the primary food of slightly older Komodos.

Information on egg incubation temperatures and raising of the young is now available from captive Komodos. While growth rates in the wild vary with food availability, young Komodos grow fast. After a few years they are too big to live in trees and start a precarious life on the ground. Females are sexually mature at 7 to 10 years and males at 8 to 11 (possibly earlier in captivity). Due to competition, wild males may not successfully breed until they are much older.

Life Span

It would initially appear that once an animal has reached adulthood it should live until old age (senescence). Apart from man, it has no obvious enemies. Yet studies show there is a continual attrition rate through adulthood. The Komodo dragon's greatest risk is other Komodo dragons. Smaller Komodos are eaten during the feeding melee around a carcass if they are not swift enough to avoid the larger, dominant animals. Water buffalo and pigs can seriously wound and even kill a Komodo dragon. Fights between Komodo dragons also cause injuries. A sick or old animal is eaten by others. Burrow collapse, starvation and dehydration also kill Komodo dragons. Fires can kill adults caught away from their burrows as well as babies. The recent decrease in total Komodo dragon numbers is partly attributed to man's poaching of deer, one of the Komodo's main food sources. It is not yet established to what extent this directly leads to the death of adults or acts to decrease their ability to reproduce.

Little is known of the role diseases and parasites play in the mortality of wild Komodo dragons, but it does not seem to be significant. The animals shed their skin regularly to remove parasites. Unlike snakes, which may shed their whole skin at once, Komodos shed theirs piece by piece.

So what is old age for a Komodo dragon? Large reptiles generally have long life spans, as evidenced by crocodiles and tortoises. Records for wild Komodo dragons do not exist, although a captured adult male lived another 25 years in captivity in Taronga Zoo, Australia. Unfortunately, there is no proven method of estimating the age of the animals. However, based on assumptions from their growth rate and age at sexual maturity, about 50 years appears to be a reasonable estimate for longevity in the wild.

Ecosystems

Like any other animal, the Komodo dragon does not live in isolation, nor has it evolved on its own. It is an integral part of its surroundings, and its existence cannot be viewed separately from the environment and ecosystem it lives in. As a voracious carnivore the Komodo plays a vital role in controlling the numbers of other species around it and hence the overall balance among them.

The Wallacea Zone

Indonesia has more mammal species than any other country. This diversity stems, in part, from the large number of ecosystems on the islands, from tropical lowland rain forest to semi-arid savannah, and

Opposite: The red-brown flowers of this orchid (Vanda sp.) *are a common sight on trees, but the much rarer yellow flower was discovered only in 1996.*

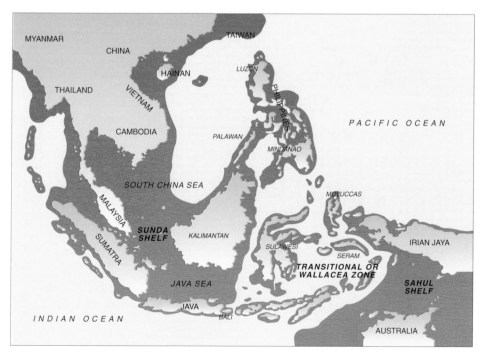

from coastal vegetation to sub-alpine and alpine environments.

The other major reason for Indonesia's great wealth of species is its location between the Asian and Australian continents. During the Pleistocene ice ages the sea level was up to 85 m lower than it is today, and Borneo, Sumatra, Java and Bali, with the rest of Southeast Asia, comprised one giant land-mass— the Sunda Shelf. Plants and animals could migrate easily from one part of the landmass to another. Consequently, the above islands have many animal types in common with the rest of Southeast Asia

Left: Cacti are found only on Rinca.
Below: The bark of the Zizyphus tree is traditionally mixed with the barks of other trees and used to cure stomach ailments.

—elephants, rhinos, pigs, tigers, monkeys and apes.

Similarly, in the east the large landmass of the Sahul Shelf included present-day Australia, the island of New Guinea and several smaller nearby islands during the same period. That explains why Australian-derived species such as tree kangaroos, cassowaries and marsupials are found in Irian Jaya, the Indonesian part of New Guinea.

But Komodo Island lies in a key position within the archipelago: at its centre. It was not linked by land to either of these great landmasses during this period. This zone in between, known as the transitional

zone or Wallacea, was named after one of the world's great naturalists, Sir Alfred Russell Wallace, a nineteenth century traveller who explored much of Indonesia seeking to understand its diversity.

Strangely, Wallace never visited Komodo Island. History may have been rewritten if he had, as the islands graphically reveal the processes and concepts he was debating.

Evolutionary biology is easiest to study on islands as their small size and relative isolation usually make evolutionary patterns more apparent. The islands of the Komodo region are important as not only do they display both Asian- and Australian-derived flora and fauna, reflecting the interface

Scattered trees dot the grassland that dominates the park.

The ripe pods of the tamarind tree (Tamarindus indicus) *are relished by both animals and man.*

between two major biogeographic areas—something Wallace was puzzling over—but they are also home to the Komodo dragon. The animal is a classic example of the tendency for reptiles to evolve towards giganticism. While Wallace was struggling to rationalise the differences in species he saw around him, the evolutionary development of the Komodo dragon poses questions scientists are still arguing over.

The plants and animals within the Wallacea zone must have either been evolving in situ for a very long period, or are more recent settlers that have been able to cross saltwater barriers. A gradual drying out of the climate has also influenced the present-day ecosystem, restricting once widespread moist forests to small pockets in wetter areas and allowing grasslands to dominate.

Island biogeography theory states that the smaller an island, the lower the variety of plants and animals it has. Combined with its limited access and dry climate, it is not surprising that the Komodo region displays fairly poor species diversity. While there are not great numbers of species, those that have managed to reach these islands and survive in the tough environment have not only shaped the development and life of the Komodo dragon but are a

Opposite: The magnificent lontar palm thrives in dry conditions. Some trees retain their lower, dead leaves, while others shed them.

fascinating mix—reflecting their varied origins—and are well worth examining further.

Vegetation

A long dry season, low rainfall and poor soil mean the vegetation cover on Komodo differs significantly from that of much of the rest of Indonesia. Trees and shrubs tend to be drought deciduous, shedding their leaves through the dry season to minimise water loss. The broad vista of savannah tenuously surviving on rocky hilltops and slopes is broken by gullies running seaward. Dry for most of the year, their position is marked by a line of green trees tapping the still-moist

Where forest and grassland meet is the favourite haunt of both deer and Komodo dragons.

soil. As the streambeds fan out they deposit scarce topsoil, allowing open forest to form. Small areas of mangrove and quasi-cloud forest dot the landscape. Each of these vegetation types is important for the different habitat it provides.

Yet much of what we observe today in the park has already been altered by man. Left untouched, the natural vegetation would be mostly monsoon forest, a mixed deciduous dry and fairly open forest, with low-branched trees and a relatively rich ground cover of herbaceous plants. Regular fires have altered this to open grassland or savannah woodland. Few new trees or shrubs are seen, as fires kill off the young growth and allow only old, established trees to survive.

Man, too, has added species of vegetation. Cactus (*Opuntia nigricans*) is the most obvious. Found only on Rinca, its method of arrival has been lost in time, but it is well suited to the arid conditions and flourishes in large clumps. Coconuts were also introduced on the islands by man, and groves mark old garden sites before park restrictions confined villagers' activities. These new species provide cover and shade but are not used much by the animals.

Savannah

Withered dry for most of the year, grasses cover about 70 percent of the park's area. The savannah includes scattered trees. As the different tree species are easier to distinguish than the grasses, they are used to describe the two principal types of savannah.

The *Zizyphus-Themeda* type is characterised by several species of *Themeda*, a tall grass reaching up to 2 m in height. It provides food for herbivores and cover for both prey and Komodo dragons. The seeds of the principal trees, *Zizyphus sp.*, turn bright red in June if allowed to ripen before being plucked by monkeys, deer, birds and civet cats who all enjoy the extra nutrition. Humans can also eat the fruit of the tree, known locally as *langka* or *bidara*, and use the bark for medicine.

Scattered, fine-leafed tamarind trees (*Tamarindus indicus*) provide welcome shade and sustenance to hikers. The ripe pods contain a refreshing sticky brown pulp, *asam*. Sold in many parts of the country, in the past it was a significant source of income for locals. The tall trees are prolific, literally covering the ground with their pods, and are an important food source for animals.

The second main type of vegetation sometimes blends with the *Zizyphus-Themeda* group but is usually distinct. It is characterised by the unmistakable, towering, pom-pom topped palm, *Borassus flabellifer* or the lontar palm. One of the most striking plants on the islands, it dots the slopes and valleys and in places stands starkly silhouetted against the skyline. Usually this vegetation supports fewer species of plants and animals than the *Zizyphus-Themeda* group, and the two grow on different soil types. The *Zizyphus-Themeda* group prefers an alluvial sandy clay, while the lontar palm thrives on rockier or clay-based ground.

The lontar palm is an important subsistence and commercial tree in eastern Indonesia. It is tapped for its sweet juice, which can be drunk straight, boiled down to make palm sugar, fed to stock, or fermented into *tuak*, a local alcoholic beverage. The natives of Komodo did not extensively tap the tree for its sugar, but they used its timber for housing and its leaves for thatching. The trees are either male or female. Only the females bear the large, dark purple fruit whose sweet, translucent flesh is relished by pigs on the islands.

Monsoon Forest

Tropical, drought-deciduous monsoon forest covers 25 percent of the park. The proportion on each island varies considerably, though, with Padar having less than 10 percent monsoon forest cover. The trees prefer the moister water courses of streambeds or foothills.

In the monsoon forest the tree canopy is higher and more continuous than in the savannah. The dominant tree species are the tamarind, *Zizyphus sp.* and *Sterculia sp.* The last, known locally as *wol* (or *kepuh*), is an important animal food source. The fist-sized seedpods, which turn red as they ripen, contain a very oily nut. Birds love it, and people roast and eat it. It can also be pounded and then squeezed to produce lamp oil. Other distinctive trees include the *kesambi* (*Schleichera oleosa*). Its leaves are used as a vegetable, the fruit is eaten, and the bark is mixed with the *Zizyphus* bark for treating stomach ailments.

Generally the forest is thorny and open. Its fringes, where it merges into grassland, are the favourite habitat for Komodo dragons to live in and reproduce. Conveniently for the Komodos, this is also where deer like to be during the day.

Quasi-Cloud Forest

Left over from a time when the region was much wetter, quasi-cloud forest covers the tops of the island's higher peaks. Different tree species thrive here. Thorny bamboo stands (*Bambusa blumeana*) flourish. Bamboo is also found in the drier areas of Flores, but it is not a preferred habitat for Komodo dragons.

Mangroves

Pockets of deep green mangrove hug the coast. Despite covering only 5 percent of the terrestrial part of the park, they are important to many animals. Rinca and parts of Flores are well endowed with mangrove, including *Rhizophora sp.* and *Lumnitzera sp.* Komodos hunt wild pig and monkeys here. Deer come, possibly seeking salt-rich foods, and water birds abound. The distinctive aerial roots of the trees help stabilise them against the wash of the waves and enable oxygen to be taken direct from the air. Mangroves help consolidate new land and protect against erosion, and the submerged tangle of roots provides a protected nursery and spawning ground for fish and shrimp.

Other Plants

In some areas close to the beach is a small zone of *Pandanus-spinifex*. Although limited in area, the plants provide critical shade for scavenging Komodo dragons.

Animals

While the Komodo dragon grabs the casual visitor's attention, there are a number of other interesting animals that the observant hiker may be lucky enough to encounter. Typical of the small islands in the Wallacea zone, there are few species of terrestrial mammals in the Komodo region—only 14 have been recorded. Birds are significantly better represented—over 72 species have been sighted within the park.

All the mammals originated in Asia, but deer, goats, water buffalo, monkeys, horses, pigs and dogs are thought to have been introduced by man some centuries ago. Most of these animals seem to have a neutral

Water buffalo graze in the early morning and late afternoon, preferring to rest near water during the day.

or positive influence on the Komodo dragon population and are permitted within the park. Hunting dogs, left after poaching raids, are the exception. They actively interfere with the Komodos, stealing food from smaller animals and scaring deer, and are being eradicated where possible. Feral cats have also arrived, but they appear to be mostly clustered around the village and ranger stations. Judging by scats the author has witnessed, these also provide tasty morsels for Komodo dragons.

Deer

Commonly seen, the Sunda Sambar deer, *Cervus timorensis floresiensis,* is a medium-sized deer. A large stag reaches 80 cm at the shoulder and may weigh a maximum of 200 kg, but hinds are considerably smaller and average 50 kg.

Known as *rusa* in Indonesia, deer breed between June and August, and fawns are born from January to May, when fresh young shoots are available for them to feed on. The hind leaves the fawn alone for the first two to five days of its life, returning just to nurse it, and Komodo dragons regularly attack the defenceless young.

Adult deer also form a favourite Komodo meal. The deer feed at night on the savannah, and in the early morning small herds of 5 to 10 animals move to the savannah hilltops. By mid-morning they move again, to the open forest to rest in the heat of the day. This daily pattern makes them vulnerable to

Distribution of Major Mammal Species

	Komodo	Rinca	Padar	Flores
Deer	•	•	•	•
Pigs	•	•		•
Water buffalo	•	•		•
Horses		•		•
Monkeys		•		•
Civet cats	•	•		•
Rodents	•	•	•	•

ambush from Komodo dragons, who hunt them mid-morning.

The relationship between the two is evident from surveys of Padar Island. Hoogerwerf, one of the first scientists to study the behaviour of wild Komodos and the ecology of the area, visited Padar in 1953. He estimated there were about 70 deer. But in 1977 van der Zon, a scientist helping put together a proposal to make the islands a national park, saw no animals or tracks. Poaching, dogs and fire are thought to have contributed to the deer's disappearance from the island. Without this source of prey Komodo dragons also died out, possibly around 1971 and certainly by 1983.

However, once the Komodos were gone, deer that reappeared on the island dramatically increased in number. Deer are known for their tendency and ability to swim to new territory, so this recolonisation is not surprising. As Komodo tracks have now been seen on Padar again, deer numbers may drop and stabilise.

Because of the close predator-prey relationship, deer poaching has been of increasing concern to park management.

Pigs

The wild pig, *Sus scrofa vittatus*, is a relatively small subspecies, weighing up to 40 to 45 kg. Called *babi* in Indonesia, wild pigs prefer the savannah/monsoon forest interface and are omnivorous. At night, when Komodos sleep, pigs clean up leftover carcasses from Komodo kills. They eat turtle eggs, another food source for Komodos, as well as Komodo dragon eggs.

The relationship between the two animals is complex. Komodo dragons eat pigs, but pigs have been known to attack adult Komodos. Villagers have reported pigs attacking solitary people.

Two to six piglets are born to each female during the rainy season. Interestingly, the nests, placed in high grasses, are not plundered by Komodo dragons, perhaps because the mother pig is such an aggressive defender of her young.

Water Buffalo

Known as *kerbau* in Indonesian, water buffalo (*Bubalus bubalis*) are more difficult to spot than deer, but their presence is obvious from droppings, well-worn trails and large mud wallows. According to villagers, a single pair were introduced on the island in the late nineteenth century. Despite making a good meal, they were not hunted and could therefore multiply. The type of buffalo found here is relatively small, with a large bull weighing just under 600 kg and a female around 400 kg. Mating occurs from March to May, and the young (30 to 40 kg) are born in January. Not surprisingly, the young are more often attacked and eaten by Komodo dragons.

Horses

Introduced on Rinca by the Sultan of Bima in the nineteenth century for breeding purposes, horses move in groups of 5 to 10. Adults stand about 1.2 m high at the shoulder and weigh about 250 kg. Foaling occurs through the year, providing a constant food supply for Komodo dragons, which harass pregnant females and attack new foals.

Monkeys

Macaca fascicularis, the crab-eating macaque or long-tailed macaque, like most macaque species, spends a lot of time feeding on the ground. This makes it vulnerable to attack, and monkey alarm calls usually indicate that a Komodo dragon is in the vicinity. Living in troupes of 8 to 30, the monkeys always stay close to fresh water and prefer mangrove, or the edge of the monsoon forest, as habitat. A large animal may be 50 cm tall and weigh 5 to 7 kg.

Flying foxes (Pteropus sp.) *often prefer isolated mangrove-covered islands as roosting sites.*

Civet Cats

A nocturnal animal a little larger than a domestic cat, the palm civet (*Paradoxurus hermaphroditus*) has beautiful, neat markings and can sometimes be seen around the ranger stations. Its midnight feasts on fruit are observed as droppings the next morning, and its characteristic pungent odour can be smelt very early along the trails. During the day it sleeps high in the branches of palm trees, or sometimes in rock piles, where it falls prey to Komodo dragons.

Rodents and Small Mammals

Rarely seen, shrews (*Crocidura sp.*) and a number of other rodents exist on the islands, playing an important role as food for small Komodo dragons. An endemic species, *Rattus rintjanus*, lives on Rinca and Padar. Known as the Rinca rat, it lives in burrows below rocks on the hillside. It emerges in the evening and moves down to the grasses of the coastal areas to feed. All these smaller animals are also important food sources for birds of prey and snakes.

Bats

At night, fishermen's lights attract insects as well as fish, and the sky comes alive with hundreds of small bats. A number of species live here, and any that roost in tree hollows may fall prey to daytime-hunting Komodo dragons.

Fruit bats (*kalong* in Indonesian) or flying foxes roost in noisy,

boisterous and smelly daytime camps, often in the top branches of mangrove trees. There is little shade, so they spend long periods grooming and cooling off by licking their wafer-thin wings and fur, allowing the moisture to evaporate.

For many years there was a bat camp close to Kampung Komodo. It has recently shifted to a less accessible site, perhaps due to disturbances from tourists clapping their hands to wake the resting bats.

Fruit bats are the world's largest bats, with an impressive wingspan of up to 1.7 m. They fly at a speed of 35 to 40 km/h, shifting from island to island searching for the fruit and flowers that make up their diet. They are found through most of Southeast Asia and northern Australia and play an important role in seed dispersal for forest trees.

Snakes, Crocodiles and Other Reptiles

The harsh environment of the Komodo area suits many reptile species other than the Komodo dragon. Tree-dwelling lizards, such as tokay and geckos, are a significant food source for small Komodos. Geckos may well surpass insects as the latter's primary food source in the middle of the dry season.

Snakes are rarely spotted by tourists travelling well-trodden paths, but many species live on the islands. More often seen in the rainy season, several, such as the white-lipped viper and sea snakes, are poisonous. The Russell's viper (*Vipera russellii limitis*) is considered the most dangerous and is greatly feared by villagers. Attractively

*Opposite: Rarely seen by tourists, snakes such as this white-lipped viper (*Trimeresurus albolabris*) are easier to spot in the rainy season.*

Lesser sulphur-crested cockatoos were once common on nearby islands, but now flocks like this are seen only in Komodo National Park.

marked with grey ovals and spots, it grows to about 3 to 4 feet in length.

The massive saltwater crocodile (*Crocodylus porosus*) was once present on these islands, but hunting has virtually eliminated it. Interestingly, reptiles such as the water monitor (*Varanus salvator*), a close relative of the Komodo, and many species of python are common in surrounding areas and similar habitats but not in the park (occasional water monitors have been recorded, but they are probably transients). Presumably they cannot compete with the Komodo dragon, a more powerful predator. In parts of Flores, where the Komodos are transient or their density lower, the territories of these animals overlap.

Birds

Compensating for the limited variety of mammals on the islands is the profusion of bird species. Eggs, hatchlings and adults are all prey to young and medium-sized Komodos who are still able to climb trees. Ground dwellers, such as the green jungle fowl (*Gallus varius*) and domestic chicken, fall victim to adult Komodos.

There is a mix of both Asian- and Australian-derived species on the islands. Perhaps the most visible Australian representatives are the lesser sulphur-crested cockatoos (*Cacatua sulphurea*). The raucous call of these large birds, flying around in small flocks, pierces the early morning tranquillity. Asian birds are well represented by groups such as orioles, sunbirds and drongos.

Often overlooked is the orange-legged scrub fowl (*Megapodius reinwardt reinwardt*—frequently misidentified as *M. freycinet*), a dull name for the fascinating creature that provides nesting sites for the Komodo dragon. This shy bird, about the size of a large chicken, spends its time foraging for insects in the leaf litter on the forest floor.

Like other birds in the Australasian megapode (giant feet) group of birds, instead of sitting on its nest to incubate eggs it lays eggs in mounds of rotting vegetation or in hot volcanic or beach sands. The species living in the park builds huge mounds of vegetation, and then the female tunnels into the top of it and lays a single egg. As the vegetation rots it creates warmth, which incubates the egg, and 50 to 70 days later a fully developed bird emerges. It is the most advanced chick in the world. Upon hatching it can run, fly and find food for itself. Given the lack of parental care, this is a sensible adaptation for a ground-dwelling bird living with Komodos!

A single egg is laid at a time, but over a season the female may lay a number of eggs. The birds mate for life and reuse the same site over years. Other megapodes may use the same nest. Mounds about 10 m across and up to 2 m high can be found scattered through the islands.

Orange-legged scrub fowl eggs are laid at a depth of 30 to 50 cm and require an incubation temperature of 32 to 34°C. As stated earlier, this temperature is higher than the preferred incubation temperature for Komodo dragons. This may explain why the Komodos seem to favour laying their eggs deeper and in old nests where the vegetation has already rotted and temperatures are cooler.

The swiftlets (*Collocalia sp.*) are of commercial value. Small quantities of their edible nests are found around the rocky islets, particularly on Padar. They are collected from August to October and provide a valuable source of income for locals; but they are found on cliff faces, and collecting them is a risky and sometimes fatal task.

Soaring majestically high above the islands are the raptors (birds of prey). The islands, with their open ground and plentiful rodents, makes hunting easy, and the isolated rocky outcrops create ideal roosting and nesting sites.

The rich chestnut of the Brahminy kite's (*Haliastur indus*) wings and upper body makes it easy to spot. Similarly patterned, but greyer and much larger (70 cm), the white-bellied sea eagle (*Haliaeetus leucogaster*) patrols both land and sea. Both birds are known to prey on young Komodos.

Nesting Turtles

Nesting turtles, which lay their eggs on beaches in the Komodo area, are important for a number of terrestrial animals. The eggs are collected by villagers and also relished by pigs, Komodo dragons and civet cats. When Komodos still lived on islands such as Padar, turtle eggs and occasionally adult turtles formed a significant part of their

Top: Insect life is most prolific in the rainy season.
Opposite: The female Nephila sp. *spider has a leg span of 7–8 cm. The male is smaller.*

diet, third in importance after deer and rats.

Marine life is discussed in detail in the next chapter.

Spiders

Scattered through the open forest/savannah areas and common throughout much of Indonesia are the massive webs of the *Nephila* spiders, members of the orb weaver family. Their rich, gold-coloured webs cover several metres and were traditionally used to dress wounds to help the blood coagulate. Many other spiders also make the islands their home, as any trailblazer on an early morning walk soon discovers.

Insects

Insect life is prolific on the islands, yet it is often overlooked. Translucent beehives hang from high branches. Leaves are bonded together by busy weaver ants to create a new home. Brown trails, the work of termites, run up almost every tree trunk. Yellow and orange butterflies flit by, and despite their beauty and delicateness, Mother Nature puts another twist in the web of life on Komodo. They are usually found perched on a pile of dung or carrion, not flowers, as they seek a meal, moisture and salt. For the Komodo dragon, the most important members of this vast group are the grasshoppers, which abound on the savannah and are an important part of the diet of small Komodos.

The Underwater World

The islands in the Komodo region are dry and harsh, but below the surface of the water the scene is the exact opposite. Reef slopes drip with colour, and marine life of all shapes and sizes enjoys the rich waters surrounding the islands. The underwater realm of Komodo National Park is considered among the most productive in the world, according to a Food and Agriculture Organisation (FAO) study. It is home to 900 to 1,000 species of fish, one of the most diverse populations in the world, and is one of the richest areas for coral in Indonesia. More than 260 hard coral species have been documented, spread across 70 genera.

The importance of the Komodo marine region within Indonesia's system of marine reserves can be properly understood only after looking at the position Indonesian coral reefs hold relative to the rest of the world. Indonesia has about one eighth of the world's coral reefs. Internationally, it is recognised as the centre for coral reef biodiversity, and this region may be thought of as the cradle of coral reef civilisation. Unfortunately, a recent World Bank study by H. Cesar shows only 29 percent of Indonesian reefs to be in good condition (and as little as 4 percent in pristine condition). However, there is increased political understanding of the situation, and Komodo National Park is benefiting from greater protection. The marine part of the park still contains some magnificent reefs, and planned management of it is now under way.

High Diversity

This incredible abundance of life is present for several reasons. Deepwater passages cut through the chain of islands that form Indonesia. Water flows from the Pacific through to the Indian Ocean (north–south) with a falling tide and brings clear water. A rising tide brings upwelling water from the south, rich in nutrients.

Currents, tides, wind patterns and local physical characteristics all make the local surface water movement complex. Currents race through at up to 8–9 knots, bringing life-giving food to the creatures in

Opposite: Underwater photographers in the Komodo area are rewarded by sights such as of these nudibranch (Chromodoris magnifica).

Tubastrea sp., *like many corals, feed at night and only then can be seen in all their glory.*

the area. The walls of the straits abound in stationary filter feeders, which spread out their tentacles to gather in the rich nutrients brought by the rushing waters.

This water, rich in oxygen, basic nutrients, salts, nitrates and phosphates, together with strong longshore currents and a limited inflow of fresh water and sediment, provides the perfect environment for coral growth. A high diversity of coral, in turn, allows a much greater variety of species to live and feed within it.

Many reef fish and invertebrates have larvae that drift with the ocean currents. Thus, the constant flow of water brings not only a stream of food but also floating larvae and microscopic young of many different species looking for suitable sites to colonise.

Perhaps most critical in securing high levels of diversity is the wide variety of ecosystems in the waters of Komodo. As on land, different species prefer slightly different conditions, and so the greater the number of ecological niches available the greater the variety of species that will be found. Water temperatures in the south may be as low as 18.5°C (65°F) in deeper water, while in the north and in warm bays it rises to 30°C (86°F). The rugged coastline provides shallow, sheltered bays, rocky headlands, isolated seamounts, sandy beaches, sea grass meadows and mangrove mudflats, as well as steep drop-offs that continue underwater and are scoured by the tidal races. Within each of these habitats there are further subdivisions based on exposure to wind, wave action and current. While divers generally confine themselves to coral reefs, many of the other zones are fascinating for the interested underwater naturalist.

Marine Creatures

Migrating whales are frequently spotted off the islands, and 14 marine mammal species have been identified in the area so far. No detailed work has yet been done on Komodo, but observations from the last remaining traditional whaling village in Indonesia, farther east at Lamalera, show that sperm whales and spinner dolphins are common catches. Lower numbers of blue, pilot and false killer whales are also caught. Sperm whales appear to be present all year, and small breeding pods are thought to be members of a larger composite stock resident in Indonesian waters. Migrations of other species seem to occur mainly in the rainy season.

Whale sharks (*Rhincodon typus*) are spotted during the rainy season, particularly in November and December. Dugong (*Dugong dugon*) are occasionally seen and tend to frequent the sea grass beds found principally in the northern and eastern parts of the park. In the past, people from Sumbawa detected them by listening for the sounds they made at the surface, and then harpooned them for food.

Turtles, particularly green and hawksbill, like to nest on the beaches on north and east Komodo and west and south Padar. Egg laying peaks in July to August and November, but occurs intermittently through much of the year, providing Komodo dragons with a significant food supply. To help preserve the nests from predation by snakes, dogs and pigs as well as Komodo dragons, the rangers have periodically constructed protective fences around them. Loggerhead, olive ridley and leatherback turtles have also been recorded swimming in these waters.

The deep, cool, richly oxygenated waters of Komodo are also home to fast swimming pelagic species. While locals are permitted to fish within the park, tourists are

Turtle numbers are decreasing across all of Indonesia, although adults such as this hawksbill turtle are still seen by divers.

restricted to outside its boundaries. Several species of tuna, Spanish mackerel, rainbow runner, kingfish, snapper, jackfish (trevally) and barracuda are caught. Pulling in a fish can be a race against time, as sharks occasionally make their presence felt by snatching a bite of the fisherman's catch.

Scientific Work

Little marine work has been done in the Komodo area despite its inclusion in the park boundaries. Now, a thorough study is being conducted by The Nature Conservancy (TNC), Jakarta, which also has a station based in Labuan Bajo. The TNC's intensive marine work (surveying 192 locations at three different depths) will provide baseline information on the marine environment. This is essential to enable park planners to detect changes over time and make informed decisions about fishing, diving, pollution, coral bleaching, sedimentation and any other marine-related issues that may arise.

Initial reconnaissance work indicates that the highest fish diversity does not coincide with the highest level of coral diversity. Coral mixed with sand and rubble patches has more fish species, presumably as there is an increased number of habitats and food available. The northern parts of Komodo and Rinca Islands rate well regarding fish diversity, as does the sheltered zone of southeast Komodo and part of east Rinca. The cooler southern waters have fewer fish species.

In terms of general underwater topography, the west coast of Flores supports a narrow fringing reef with some patches of mangrove. Numerous islands and reefs within the park's designated buffer zone have shallow, extensive reef platforms, and the area has a high variety of habitats and corals. Good coral cover exists around the northern part of Komodo Island and Gili Banta (outside the park boundaries) as well as in the buffer zone. Gili Banta is an excellent dive site for fish as well as having wonderful hard and soft corals. There is a high density of soft coral in some areas, probably due to the species' greater ability to regrow after bombing damage. Small patches of dense sea grass also exist.

The southern ends of Rinca and Komodo and the west of Komodo are rugged, steep, wave-battered coastlines. Cliffs descend directly into the sea. Gili Motang is exposed to the full force of the strong southeast swell and winds and so has a similar topography, except for a beach and coral area in the sheltered northwest. The areas tend to be difficult to access, due to wave action, but produce some excellent dives. The sheer underwater walls are festooned with invertebrate life, and there is a chance to see good-sized fish and sharks.

The east coast of Komodo is dominated by a bay, Loh Lawi.

Opposite top: Hundreds of sea cucumbers (Synaptula sp.) can be found grazing on the sides of barrel sponges, feeding on surface detritus and substances secreted by the sponges.
Opposite bottom: Unlike most corals, the calcareous skeleton of the organ pipe coral, Tubipora, always maintains its deep, rich colour.

Huge schools of small fish cluster for protection from predators that cruise the open waters around the reef.

Quieter waters and a muddy bottom decrease the number of hard corals, as these require sunlight for the zooxanthellae within them to photosynthesise. Although the coral diversity is moderate, the attractive reef topography combined with abundant filter feeders such as gorgonians, basketstars and crinoids makes for some good dive sites.

Other areas of the park vary from moderate to low coral cover, although again small zones in these areas can make wonderful dive sites due to interesting topography and an abundance of certain species.

Diving
To find the best dive locations, exact sites must be known. The comments above are conclusions drawn from the detailed TNC work done. None of the areas are identical in their underwater life, partly due to the complex topography of the region but also because of localised explosions or cyanide damage.

For photographers and those interested in marine life, the region is truly paradise. Unfortunately, the diving is not always straight-forward. Ripping waters, with whirlpooling down currents and equally savage upwellings, make certain dive sites impossible except at slack water (if it exists). Many sites are unsuitable for beginners, but for the more experienced diver they are magnificent. Seamounts rising from the ocean floor to near the surface provide some of the most stunning and exciting dives. As the infrastructure improves, Komodo is fast becoming a sought after dive location because of its relatively pristine nature, abundance of fish and marine life and variety of sites. Due to the prevailing weather conditions, it can be hard to dive both the north and south dive zones on one trip.

The rich, food-bearing tides mean that visibility is often less than ideal, rarely greater than 30 m (100 feet) and sometimes just a few arm lengths. The water is generally warmer and clearer (26 to 28°C and 15 to 30 m vis.) on the northern side, while both figures drop on the southern side (22 to 24°C and very variable visibility). At these temperatures it is preferable to have a wet suit, and possibly a hood, rather than a Lycra suit.

Wrecks exist, but they are rarely dived by tourists. Pearl fishermen usually know the exact locations, as they claim the undersides of wrecks are good collecting places for oysters. Of most interest is the wreck of an old VOC, a Dutch East Indies boat sunk on the southwest of Komodo Island at a location named after it, Soq Belanda (meaning Dutch Bay). Jacques Cousteau has visited the site twice, and according to local villagers who showed him the wreck, many treasures, including a pistol, have been retrieved from it.

Exploitation of Resources

The richness of the underwater realm is clear from the number of fishermen it attracts. Not only do locals derive their income from it, but fishermen from much farther afield are also arriving as their own areas get depleted.

Bagans (boats with lift nets) are the most visible fishing boats. At night, in front of Kampung Komodo, over a hundred may stretch across the water. Three to six men work each boat, using lights to attract squid (*cumi-cumi, Loligo sp.*) and small fish to their nets. The squid season runs from September to May, peaking in the rainy season; most of the squid is dried and sold to traders. As the squid are pelagic, the damage to the marine environment is not substantial.

Other catches are fish and shrimp. The fish may be salted and dried or sold fresh. Juvenile shrimp are caught in the mangroves from March to June and made into fermented shrimp paste (*terasi*). Specially shaped fine nets are used in shallow water to collect *nener* (juvenile *Chanos chanos, bandeng* or milkfish). This activity started in 1990, when regular flights from Bima and Labuan Bajo allowed the fish to be flown to the east Java area, where they are cultured in ponds until they reach edible size.

The catching of marine organisms from rock pools at low tide is a traditional fishing technique known as *meting*. Groups of 5 to 10 people usually travel to a beach and stay there for 7 to 10 days. Sea cucumbers, seaweed, shells, green snails (*batu laga*), abalone (*mata tujuh*) and mussels are collected, as well as mangrove timber for firewood. While *meting* is a traditional, small-scale technique, its localised impact can be severe as corals are overturned with wooden spears or iron bars and smashed in the process. In addition, the fishermen leave behind unsightly litter and campfires that sometimes burn into the nearby forest. Lately, significantly more damage is being caused as villagers from outside the park, tempted by the high price of abalone, have started entering the park and using compressors to work the underwater reefs in the same way.

Using compressors to collect oyster shells, local divers (many from Rinca) supply two pearl culture farms, one at Loh Kima and the other at Seraya Kecil. Although there is now technology to reproduce oysters in a farmed environment, the farms still collect

them from the wild. The unfortunate consequence of this practice is the high number of deaths and permanent injuries sustained by pearl divers, who lack good equipment and a knowledge of safe diving practices. Place names such as Dead Man's Point, off Rinca, are an indication of the tough life the pearl divers lead. They also collect other items of value, such as black coral (*tali laut*), even though this is a protected species in Indonesia.

Lobster and live fish are captured with the use of a cyanide solution. Live fish are taken for both the marine aquarium trade and for food. Groupers and Napoleon wrasse are targeted for overseas restaurants, mostly in Hong Kong and Taiwan. The cyanide solution

Bagans *(boats with lift nets) are the most visible fishing boats.*

has a rapid narcotising effect, stunning the animal and making it easy to catch. But this technique increases the mortality of the whole marine community. The coral reef dies, initially bleaching white, then becoming overgrown with brown algae. While this fishing method was widespread 5 to 10 years ago, it is now illegal, and protection within the park boundaries has improved. The method is used today mainly to catch lobster for the hotel and restaurant trade in Bali.

Dynamite or fertiliser (ammonium nitrate) is used for explosive fishing through much of the Indonesian archipelago. Banned in 1985, explosive fishing is still done in many areas where there is little enforcement of regulations. Fishermen drop bombs on schools of fish, usually in shallow water or near the surface (but sometimes at depths of up to 25 m). Divers then jump overboard and collect the dead or stunned fish. Large numbers of unwanted and juvenile fish are killed in the process, and the coral is shattered into small pieces, reducing the reef to rubble.

From 1950 to 1980 most of the villagers around Komodo National Park engaged in some explosive fishing, but a greater understanding of its harmful effects on the environment and increased patrolling (as well as a number of arrests) have substantially decreased the practice within the park. The presence of tourist boats also tends to discourage illegal fishing, and visitors are encouraged to report any bombing or poisoning of fish to the park staff.

The Future

Continued human pressure on marine resources is an ongoing issue. Explosive fishing and the use of cyanide solution continue to be the two most significant threats to the underwater realm, although their incidence has decreased. There have been recent disturbing reports of fishermen using pesticides and herbicides in a manner similar to cyanide. The long-term effects of these chemicals are likely to be severe, and it is hoped that these practices can be quickly stamped out. The TNC and PHPA are working together to encourage more sustainable means of livelihood for the fishermen.

TNC's establishment of a system of mooring buoys to prevent anchor damage at popular dive and snorkel sites is helping to maintain specific reefs. To some extent, the strong currents and difficult waters of the park have provided natural protection. Seamounts and steep dropoffs swept by strong currents cannot be easily exploited and have, therefore, remained pristine areas. As many underwater species have larvae that drift on the ocean currents, these protected areas can help restock and recolonise damaged zones.

Living with the Komodo Dragon

The people living within the realm of the Komodo dragon can be split into three main groups: the indigenous inhabitants of Komodo Island, known as the Ata Modo; the present-day villagers; and the rangers. Little is known about the Ata Modo, who are in many ways the most fascinating in terms of their traditions and mythology concerning the island and the Komodo dragon. Always unfortunately small in number, they have now virtually vanished, thanks to a tide of immigration. Few of the present-day villagers are of Ata Modo origin.

People of the Past—The Ata Modo

Many writers claim that Kampung Komodo was recently settled by immigrant fishermen or as a penal colony by the Sultan of Bima, who banished offenders to the desolate place. If either of these scenarios were correct, the language spoken by the people of Komodo would be the same as that of the place they originated from. Yet linguistic studies show the Ata Modo speech to be a distinctive language, not found elsewhere but derived from Flores and now incorporating many Bima and Manggarai words brought by recent immigrants.

For a distinct language to develop, a population must have been separated from other groups for a very long period of time. In this case, it does not necessarily mean that the Ata Modo always lived on Komodo Island. It could be that the entire population speaking this language migrated to the island or that any remnant population that spoke the same language either subsequently migrated or died out.

Besides the isolated nature of Komodo Island, there are several reasons for the dearth of knowledge about the Ata Modo. They were hill people who did not generally associate with coastal immigrants or traders. Poor agriculture and probable inbreeding meant the population was never large. Problems with slave raiding in the last century further decimated the numbers, and now, with the influx of outsiders and resultant interbreeding, there are no people

Opposite: Pak Ishaka Mansour from Kampung Komodo carves wood he purchased in Flores into souvenir Komodo dragons.

of pure Ata Modo blood left. According to villagers, the last one, Seganung, died in the early to mid-1970s. Unfortunately, Seganung had no children (it was common among the Ata Modo to have few or no children).

He, like all his people, was physically distinctive, with the purported traits of the Ata Modo not easily visible in present-day mixed-blood villagers. For instance, they had long ears and the lobes were further stretched by heavy earrings. They are also said to have been very tall, "more than 2 m, taller than tourists".

Historically Komodo was the only island in the region inhabited by the Ata Modo, and as today's schoolchildren learn Indonesian and satellite dishes beam in local soap operas, the few remaining part-Ata Modo people are losing the struggle to maintain their links with their culture and language.

A Brief History

The history of the Ata Modo is handed down by word of mouth, since they have no written language. J. Verheijen, a Dutch linguist and anthropologist, was one of the first foreigners to study the people, in 1977. Based primarily on his linguistic studies, he claims that they have a history going back about 2,000 years, not necessarily beginning on Komodo Island but probably at Warloka, west Flores. Supporting this, the people today say, "Our skin is close to Manggarai" and consider their *rumah adat* (the home of their traditions) to be in west Flores.

Little is known of the community before nearby kingdoms, which did record their history, started to assert their power in the region. The powerful Makassarese kingdom of Goa, based in southern Sulawesi, controlled neighbouring Sumbawa in the early 1600s. It was resoundingly beaten by the Dutch in 1669, causing a mass exodus of Makassarese refugees. They and nearby Bugis settled where they could, some of them on Komodo Island, but many turned to pirating as a livelihood.

The influence of the Sultan of Bima, east Sumbawa, strengthened, and in 1727 he claimed Manggarai. This area, and therefore Komodo, remained under Bimanese control until 1929, and the Ata Modo regarded Bima as their political centre. The island was used as a halfway shelter during storms, as a place to collect fresh water and food and for limited trading. But the convoluted coastline of Komodo also provided a safe haven for pirates, who raided Sumba for slaves before trading their catches farther west. A few were probably residents of Komodo. According to Dutch records, the local Ata Modo were also attacked by slave traders. Frustrated by their lack of defences, they moved away from the island.

In 1847, according to R. Needham's historical analysis, the islanders, "… a group of at most one hundred persons—had left Komodo for Bima, where they settled. In 1855, Komodo was reported as uninhabited." However, some of the people returned to the island a few decades later.

Remnants of old villages, hidden high in the hills, are very difficult to find now.

Needham's contention is strongly denied by the local people today. They claim that the Ata Modo have always lived on the island, perhaps because it strengthens their claim to traditional land rights within Komodo National Park. These two differing accounts can perhaps be reconciled, as some people may have moved to the protected town of Bima while others stayed on Komodo, shifting farther into the hills, where there were old, less visible villages.

Confusion may also have arisen because the villages on Komodo Island have not remained static over time. Earlier there were several villages and temporary sites used for the seasonal collection of forest products. Until about 40 years ago Kampung Komodo, currently the only village on the island, was also a garden for the hill villages.

The settling of the island is recorded in legend, as reflected in a local story cited by Needham. "At first there were only Komodo people on the island; then there came a Sumbanese, followed in turn by a man from Manggarai, some Ambonese, people from Kapu (the western part of Bajo, in western Manggarai), Sape, Bugis and others from Welak in the interior of Manggarai."

This listing is important, as the land on Komodo is divided among the 'founding clans': Modo, Sumba, Welak, Ambon and Kapu. The people of Sape, also one of the founding clans, and their descendants did not get any land but

The Muslim village of Kampung Komodo, long and narrow, hugs the coastline.

received the rights to the gebang palm trees, from which a food staple similar to sago is made.

The reasons for the granting of land to immigrants are also explained. G. Forth summarises the commonly told story: "... the first Sumbanese to land on Komodo was a 'medicine-man' who helped a woman in delivery, as a result of which both she and her child survived the birth. Because of this, the Sumbanese was invited to stay on Komodo, and a part of the island, the region called Wau, was given to him."

Before this, according to legend, the inhabitants of Komodo were unfamiliar with the normal method of delivery, and a child was brought into the world by performing an operation that invariably killed the mother. No wonder their population remained low! Childless couples sometimes still hold a ritual, "the calling of the ancestor-mother of Sumba in the place of Wau", to promote fertility.

Ata Modo Myths and Legends Involving the Komodo Dragon

Like many ethnic groups within Indonesia, the descendants of the Ata Modo have retained their ancient beliefs while being staunchly Muslim. They consider nature to be an inheritance from their ancestors, which must be protected and cared for. Anthropological work by Rafael Karjon reveals that they believe in three main supernatural forces: Ina Kama, who protects the people and the whole island; Ina Babu, who protects the Komodo dragon and its twin brother, the Ata Modo; and Ina Hadija, who protects the water sources and the whole community. Rituals and offerings are made to these three to ensure that harmony continues.

The relationship overseen by Ina Babu refers to an ancient myth claiming that the Komodo dragon and the Ata Modo are kin. Both are believed to have been created at the same time in the following way (slightly different versions of this story exist): The beautiful spirit-woman Putri Naga (also called Ompu Naga) appeared to a man,

Najo, living on Komodo Island. They married, and she subsequently gave birth to twins. The first baby was a Komodo dragon, while the second was a human. Embarrassed, the mother did not return to her husband or the village, but lived in a cave in the forest. After a few years the Komodo dragon went its own way and the child founded the Ata Modo clan.

Building rituals around dangerous animals, locations or situations is relatively common in different societies. It allows people a means of explaining, learning about and avoiding certain dangers. The Ata Modo believe that if they do not look after their twin brother they will bring danger to themselves. Hence, in the past, after every

Buildings are on stilts to discourage Komodo dragons from entering.

hunt or fish catch a portion of meat was left for the Komodo (usually the head and intestines of wild animals). However, the feeling is much broader than this. The Ata Modo feel that their future is intertwined with that of the Komodo dragon and that if the latter were to become extinct so would they.

This belief is still prevalent. Several people witnessed two adult Komodo dragons climbing out of the sea at Sape, in neighbouring Sumbawa, in the early 1980s. Around this time, government officials were discussing clearing the park of human inhabitants. The Sape people, familiar with the beliefs of the Ata Modo, interpreted the sight of the animals coming ashore as a verification of the link between them and the Ata Modo. It was perceived as a sign of support from the Komodo dragons for the people's claim to remain on the island. Since they were kin, if the people were made to leave, so would the Komodos. Sceptics suggest that the Komodo dragons may have fallen off a passing boat, as occasionally animals are smuggled off the islands for sale on the black market.

The Ata Modo also believe that the Komodo dragon will not harm them if they perform the appropriate rituals. This belief is used to explain why recent Komodo attacks have been only on foreigners and people from Rinca. It was also used to explain to the author the unusual photos obtained by Nicole Viloteau in the early 1990s. She stroked adult Komodo dragons without being attacked. While she claims it was because of her special relationship with them, the villagers say she was taken to a sacred site and was accepted as an Ata Modo before she posed for the shots. Scientists and rangers have a series of other explanations. Whatever the explanation, the fact remains that she was extremely lucky to have avoided attack, and within Indonesia the shots are considered highly inappropriate and misleading.

Lifestyle

In the past the Ata Modo were small-scale farmers who led a fairly self-sufficient life, collecting products from the forest. They carried out a limited trade in products such as tamarind pulp, lontar palm leaves, beeswax and honey, and fished from dugouts close to the beach. However, with tightened government restrictions on the use of the forest and the terrestrial part of the park, and increasing numbers of immigrant fishermen settling on the island, the main source of income for present-day villagers is marine resources.

There is not much income from tourism on Komodo Island. Goats are no longer sold to tourists for staged feedings. Instead, a little money comes from boat rental. A co-operative manages the Loh Liang ranger station cafeteria and sells small souvenirs made of wood and mother-of-pearl, with the park authority and the villagers splitting the profits. Some villagers also help during busy times by guiding tourists in the park.

As tourism has escalated, escorting trekkers has become a major part of a ranger's job.

Present-day Villagers

Recent immigration has swelled the population within the park and virtually extinguished the Ata Modo. It is not clear how many criminals and political exiles from Bima were ever sent to the island or how many remained, but social practices encouraged people to stay. Unlike in many other parts of Indonesia, where a bride moves to the village of the groom, a man from outside who marries a local girl is supposed to stay on Komodo.

In the last 50 years the island's population has increased dramatically. In 1930 there were 143 inhabitants. In 1977 there were 529. By 1993 the figure had jumped to 1,100. Most of this increase is through immigration.

Kampung Komodo is a Muslim village with a pipeline bringing fresh water from Wae Sadrap 2.5 km away, an elementary school, a PHPA guard-post, a first aid post (Puskesmas) and a police station. Houses are built on stilts, partly due to the influence of Bugis architecture and partly to avoid Komodo dragon attacks. Goats and chickens are fenced in underneath the houses at night. Some people use this area during the day to do household chores or to work on carving Komodo dragon figures from local woods for the tourist market. As most men are night fishermen, they rest during the day.

A few Ata Modo have moved to Kampung Rinca, but most of this village's inhabitants are of Bima or Bajo origin. The village was established after Kampung Komodo, but still well before the gazetting of the park. There were 250 people living there in 1930, and now there are about 700. Juvenile milkfish are collected near the beach with nets, and some men work as divers supplying the pearl culture farms with mother-of-pearl shells.

Nearby Kampung Kerora was established around 1930 and has a current population of over 200. The people are less dependent on the sea and carry out small-scale agriculture.

Rangers use a simple forked stick as protection against the Komodo dragon. The fork is pushed against the Komodo's neck to redirect the animal.

To minimise human encroachment, settlements in the park are restricted to those that can prove they were there prior to the area being declared a reserve. Thus, more recent villages on Rinca, such as Loh Baru (established in 1938) and Tambora, have been declared illegal and removed.

Two villages exist in the buffer zone of the park: Pulau Papagaran (700 inhabitants) and Pulau Mesah (1,500 inhabitants). The people from these villages often fish within the park boundaries, as do other fishermen from outside the park.

There are literally hundreds of small villages scattered through the broken range of the Komodo dragon on Flores. The spread of agriculture is a significant problem for the

Komodos here, pushing them into smaller isolated habitats and at times causing conflict. Komodo dragons occasionally attack villagers or their stock, and frustrated locals resort to poisoning or killing Komodos in their vicinity.

Rangers

Despite a long history of protection (see the first chapter), the first management unit was not established on the island until 1984, several years after the inception of Komodo National Park. Now there are 11 guard posts, all of which are connected by radio communications to park headquarters at Labuan Bajo, and boats are used to help in their patrolling and other work.

Sixty rangers are employed in the field and another 31 at park headquarters (1996 figures). The guards work for three weeks and then get a week off to return to their families (mostly in Labuan Bajo) and report to park headquarters. Apart from guiding tourists, the main part of their work involves anti-poaching patrols, fire control and general land management. Over the years they have also developed a significant infrastructure and carried out maintenance and improvements on tracks and water supply.

Rangers also conduct important flora and fauna inventories. For instance, they undertake an annual survey of Komodo dragon numbers as well as ad hoc surveys on the numbers of prey and other species. Because the rangers walk around the park each day, they know the area well and are valuable assistants to scientific researchers who come for short periods to undertake more difficult or intensive work. In turn, these visiting scientists provide rangers with much-needed training in scientific methodology.

A *kadre konservasi* (conservation corps) has been formed to help cope with the rangers' high workload, to help the villagers gain an increased environmental understanding and to provide additional employment opportunities. Fifteen villagers from Kampung Komodo have been hired to work in the cafeteria and help escort tourists to Banu Nggulung during busy times. They currently work alternate weeks. Other areas have also employed *kadres*.

Conservation of the Park

Komodo National Park was formally established on March 6, 1980, but the actual protection provided has changed according to the acknowledged needs of the time, as with most parks. Home to one of Indonesia's most famous animals, the park's importance is now well recognised. But the Komodo dragon's numbers continue to drop, and the park continues to be threatened by various factors.

In the park's early years the main issue was management of the Komodo dragon and deer habitat. It was crucial to eliminate dogs, decrease burning of grasslands and control deer poaching. Later, human encroachment emerged as a serious issue, after it started to impact on both the marine and the land environment. In the 1980s the proliferation of tourists posed another problem.

The goals of the park were redefined to:
* maintain the essential ecological processes of the environment,
* preserve the genetic diversity of the park, and

* provide for continued use of the park.

A 25-year plan is being drawn up to improve park management, taking into account both terrestrial and marine aspects. It addresses such topics as the enforcement and legal issues surrounding the park (including boundaries and zoning of areas for different uses), promotion of cooperation with the local people (including helping to provide alternative means of livelihood for those displaced by the park) and the management of the park's natural resources (including continued monitoring and research).

Lack of Knowledge
Present trends in the Komodo dragon population are not known with any certainty. Insufficient data are being collected, and there is an urgent need for more research.

Using available data, if the estimated present population of 3,000 Komodo dragons is correct, and the ratio of males to females is 3.4:1, as suggested by Auffenberg (virtually all scientists have found an uneven sex ratio although the figure varies), there is a total of 680

Opposite: Tourism focuses heavily on the Komodo dragon, but the islands themselves are alluring.

Threats to Komodo National Park

Issue	Problem	Effect
Removal of Komodo dragons	Smuggling—black market	Decreased numbers of wild Komodos
	Occasional collection for zoos/research	Decreased numbers of wild Komodos
Fire	Natural fires, those set by poachers or campfires that accidentally spread	Occasionally kill adult & baby Komodo dragons. Decreased monsoon forest habitat Increased runoff & siltation, killing coral
Tourism	Anchor damage to coral	Marine damage
	Possible pollution from cruise ships	Environmental damage
	Increased number of divers	Marine damage
	Increasing demands on rangers & park infrastructure	Fewer resources for other park activities, at least in the short term
	Large numbers of visitors at one time	Impact on aesthetic quality of park
Increasing human population	Increased agricultural areas in Flores	Decreased Komodo dragon habitat
	Increased deer hunting	Less food for Komodos & problems with feral dogs
	Increased demand for fresh water	Current shortage— due to, & affecting, villagers & tourism
	Pollution, litter & garbage	Unsightly & cause terrestrial & marine damage. Also affect health of wildlife.
	Mangrove destruction	Increased siltation; no nursery ground for fish & shrimp; removes erosion protection.
	Overfishing	Marine damage

females. The number must be broken down further into geographically separated populations. Komodo Island would have about 360 females and Rinca about 250. But small localities like Gili Motang would have only 16 (out of a total population of 70). Some pockets on Flores are believed to have even smaller populations. Since not all these females would be capable of breeding, the imbalance in the sex ratio is increased.

These statistical calculations are based on the most reliable data available. However, because of the difficulty in sexing Komodos and the lack of knowledge on the rate at which they reproduce in the wild (Auffenberg, based on a total population of around 5,000 Komodo dragons, estimated that around 1,500 babies were born each year but few survived to adulthood), the figures are best taken as a guide showing the desperate need for more work so that informed decisions can be made by park management. Much more detailed statistical analysis has been done by the Captive Breeding Specialist Group, but until accurate inputs are known the output is highly questionable.

Specific research to determine the reproductive ecology of the species is crucial. Studies need to be done on the life span of the Komodo dragon, the breeding participation rates of the animal and the sex ratio both at hatching and in adulthood, to better establish the true breeding population of Komodo dragons at each location. Genetic work determining the population diversity is also essential.

To understand what the long-term implications of any changes are for the Komodo and the ecosystem it is unavoidably tied to, research is needed on the Komodos' numbers, daily activities, home ranges, food habits, foraging behaviour and metabolic rates. Little work has been done on the life of a young Komodo dragon. Understanding the importance of the macro- and micro-habitats of the animals and their prey, and the relationship between the Komodo dragon nesting sites and the megapode bird nesting sites, will allow more detailed decisions to be made concerning the preservation and management of habitats.

Ecotourism

As humans put increased pressures on the land, national parks around the world are finding that they increasingly have to justify their existence in economic terms as well as aesthetic. Ecotourism is a much vaunted solution and has certainly become a major issue for park management at Komodo National Park.

In the early 1970s adventurers started to arrive in groups. They stayed for just a few hours, brought their own goats with them and left little trace of their visits. In 1975, 367 tourists came to the island. In the financial year 1995–96 over 29,000 people visited. Day visitors are still in the majority, with only 30 percent staying overnight.

Foreigners account for 80 to 90 percent of visitors. Over 200 people

Carefully controlled tourism is a positive experience for everyone.

per day is common through the peak season of July–August, which puts great pressure on park resources. High visitor numbers require greater numbers of rangers to act as guides, and tourism groups are pressing the park to improve the facilities and services. Luckily the impact on the Komodo dragons and their habitat is relatively minimal. Some soil erosion occurs on paths, but rainfall is low and this is not a serious issue. Tourism impacts on the small portion of the park that is regularly used for trekking, but most of the park is not frequented by tourists.

Still, demand and expectations are rising. Visitors to Komodo and its adjacent islands are expected to continue to increase dramatically as the area becomes more accessible, infrastructure improves and television documentaries increase knowledge of the animal and the great beauty of the area.

Apart from the provision of trails, accommodation and interpretative material, the biggest problem in the past has been associated with goat feeding. Early visitors wanted maximum action and numbers, and

watching goat-gobbling Komodos became the norm. It interfered with the behaviour patterns of the Komodos in the area. They no longer hunted but gathered in large groups, waiting for easy food. As a better understanding of the situation developed, park authorities realised the importance of keeping the park in as natural a state as possible to achieve their overall management goals. In 1988 feeding was cut back and permitted only on Wednesdays and Sundays. It was then reduced to once a week and finally stopped altogether in 1994, although a number of tourists would like to see the gory staged feedings continue.

Fears that tourists would no longer be able to see a Komodo dragon were groundless. The number that they saw just dropped from 15–20 to a realistic 2–3. The improvement of the water hole at Banu Nggulung ensured that natural game would be attracted to the site, so now even without the artificial inducement of goats Komodos are common in the area.

Since it is hoped that tourism will bring much needed economic development to the area, it is essential to improve the experience for the visitor. Better guiding and interpretative materials are required. The level of tourism can be increased in a sympathetic way by careful planning. As most tourists stay less than one day, adding to the range of options in the region through sea kayaking, sailing, trekking, sport fishing, diving, bird watching and particularly cultural tours is seen as a way to improve the development of the region.

The flow of money also needs assessing. Benefits already accrue in neighbouring towns (food and accommodation, rental of boats), but much of the money does not flow to the park inhabitants. Living within or next to the park, these are the people who can either see the benefits of the park and help monitor and patrol it, or who return to using its resources, adding to the problems and destruction. By increasing the economic benefits local people derive from the establishment of the park, the task of park management will become much easier.

Goat feeding has stopped now that there is an increased understanding of its negative impact on the Komodos' behaviour.

The Future

The steps presently being taken to conserve the park and the Komodo dragon lead to optimism for the future. But the optimism must be tempered by the uncertainties and lack of knowledge outlined above. The isolated populations of the Komodo are small and may be unable to recover from even low levels of disruption or removal. Theoretical and historical analyses of island populations show that large carnivores with small geographically separated populations face one of the highest risks of extinction since they cannot always adjust to changes in their environment. The tough-looking Komodo dragon, which has survived geological upheaval and a drying out of its climate, may be far more susceptible than we realise.

Komodo Dragons in Captivity

Ever since their discovery, Komodo dragons have been considered an oddity. Despite being not very active animals, they have always been a prime draw at zoos.

The first international zoo to display a live Komodo dragon was Bronx Zoo, New York, in 1926. Two animals were on show there, but both died within two months. Komodo dragons can now be seen at zoos in the United States, Europe, Asia and Australia. As of December 1995, there were 191 registered in zoos. Of these, 36 were caught in the wild and the remainder were bred in captivity.

Their life span in captivity has increased dramatically. Taronga Zoo in Sydney, Australia, holds the record for Komodo dragon longevity—a male, Keith, arrived as an adult in 1963 and lived for 25 more years.

As the Indonesian government has recognised the uniqueness of the species and the need for its protection, stronger controls have been placed on exports. With Komodo dragons being bred in captivity, the pool of animals and the number on display is rapidly rising. At first glance it would seem that this should decrease the demand for wild specimens. However, there is an ongoing debate between captive breeding specialists, who want to capture more animals in order to help improve the gene pool in zoos, and conservationists, who argue that the long-term protection of the species is better ensured by using the scarce resources to protect the existing wild population *in situ*, and save its habitat and other species at the same time. There is general agreement that the collection of young specimens, which have a naturally high mortality rate, is less damaging than the taking of mature Komodo dragons.

Setting aside this complex argument, there is no doubt that zoo animals are easier to observe and often become accustomed to being handled, making certain information easier to gather. For instance, their sensitivity to temperature change can be clearly seen. Komodos prefer to stay under strategically placed heat lamps in

Opposite: Pak Agustinus Kevkole, a keeper at Taman Safari Park just outside Jakarta, monitors the health of this one-and-a-half-year-old.

Like all well-fed reptiles, captive Komodo dragons spend most of their time resting.

zoos in colder climates. In tropical Singapore, when it starts to rain and the temperature drops, Komodo dragons immediately move into their pool, which is warmer and at a constant temperature.

Scientists have also discovered more specific information about the anatomy and physiology of the Komodo dragon. For instance, access to unfiltered sunlight is important as the UV rays help build up the animal's calcium levels.

Despite all its advantages, study of captive animals does not replace the need for research on wild animals. It may raise questions, but it is incorrect to transfer observations of captive, habituated animals to those in the wild. For instance, the issue of pair bonding discussed on page 37 remains a mystery. A study by the Friends of the Zoo (Sahabat Satwa) at Ragunan Zoo on seven Komodos kept in one cage showed that unconsummated pairing occurred from January to October, although successful mating occurred only between the months of June and October. It is not known whether the former matings are normal behaviour reinforcing pair bonding or whether they were brought on by the artificial situation of a female unable to escape a male's attention.

Breeding Results

Undoubtedly the greatest zoo success has been the provision of suitable conditions for mating, successful egg laying and hatching, and raising of the young.

Only recently has regular, successful breeding occurred. This is partly due to the difficulty in distinguishing between males and females. Several zoos worked for years on mating programs, only to discover that they were dealing with two Komodos of the same sex! Indonesian zoos were the first to breed captive Komodo dragons, presumably because they had a climate and surroundings similar to the animals' natural environment, plus they had far more of the animals than other sanctuaries did.

Komodo mating and egg laying were first reported at Surabaya Zoo in 1937, but it was not until 1968 that the zoo had its first hatchlings. In 1982 another 8 babies were recorded hatching from 24 eggs. In 1994 Gembira Loka Zoo, Jogya-

The growth of this baby, born in Ragunan Zoo, Jakarta, is closely monitored.

karta, Central Java, reported 28 hatchlings (4 of which subsequently died), probably from at least two clutches. Jakarta's zoos also had some success. Batavia Zoo had its first captive-born babies in 1941, and the following year 25 young Komodo dragons were hatched. This zoo no longer exists, but Ragunan Zoo hatched young in 1989. Unfortunately, in most cases no detailed records were kept and little additional scientific information was gained from these breeding efforts.

The National Zoological Park in Washington, DC, was the first outside Indonesia to successfully breed Komodo dragons, and it made a detailed study of the process. Two young animals, Sobat

Obesity in captive animals is more than just a problem of appearance: it affects the health of the animals and may inhibit the development of eggs in females.

and Friendty, were presented by Indonesia's President Soeharto to President Bush in May 1988. On January 20, 1992, Sobat laid a clutch of 26 fertile eggs. Since then she has produced many more clutches, not always with the same male.

Unlike in Indonesian zoos, where incubation was allowed to take place naturally below ground level, in the US the eggs were artificially incubated. This made data collection much easier. Sufficient moisture was essential to prevent the eggs from drying out through their leathery shells, and the eggs were kept at temperatures of 27.5 to 29°C. Cooler incubation temperatures resulted in longer incubation times, but on average the eggs took 7 to 8.5 months to hatch.

After hatching, most babies consumed their own afterbirth, which remained in the egg, but then refused food for up to two weeks. When they did eat, they favoured small animals, such as a cricket or a young furred mouse, but frequently the keeper had to kill the creature and cut it open, revealing the innards, to finally tempt the baby to feed. Scientists believe that wild behaviour may be similar to this. Wild newborn babies may not feed for the first couple of weeks and then prefer to take dead or injured animals rather than hunt. A young Komodo dragon could be severely bitten if it hunted rodents, and that may explain why it eats safe food, such as small invertebrates and eggs, for the first few months.

While still small, the zoo animals were fed a mouse every five days. The babies were initially very tame and allowed keepers to handle them, but after a month they became more aggressive and threatened and bit their keepers.

Zoo Problems

In the early years, animals in captivity did not fare well. Many deaths were due to an inadequate knowledge of Komodo dragon husbandry, hygiene and veterinary care. The animals like hot weather, and kept in unsuitable conditions they generally succumbed to enteritis, intestinal infections or sometimes a very rapid ecto-parasitic buildup. Another reason for the high mortality was that in the past large animals were collected. These mature animals did not adjust to captivity as well as the younger, smaller Komodo dragons collected later.

With increased understanding and care, most zoos now have few problems; and kept well, Komodos appear to be quite resistant. Food is presented as whole animals, or parts thereof, consisting of skin, bone, fur or feathers and stomach contents, so that it closely replicates wild food. However, just as in the wild, fighting between individuals can cause serious injuries.

Obesity is another issue with Komodos in captivity. They do not need to exert themselves to obtain food and instead spend their time resting. Considering that Komodo dragons travel up to 10 km per day in the wild and that they have evolved to store surplus food in case it is some time before the next meal, regular feeding quickly leads to obesity.

Visiting the Komodo Dragons

Travelling to Komodo Island has never been easy. There are hair-raising stories of adventurers setting out on unseaworthy boats, but for most people just seeing the Komodo dragons and walking in the park is adventure enough.

Opposite: Magnificent views reward those prepared to do a little hiking.

There is no airstrip in the park. Heliports do exist for emergencies and visiting dignitaries, but tourists enter from either Sumbawa in the west or Flores in the east, or travel on organised tours on local boats or larger cruise ships.

Being an ecotourist means more than just visiting, admiring and

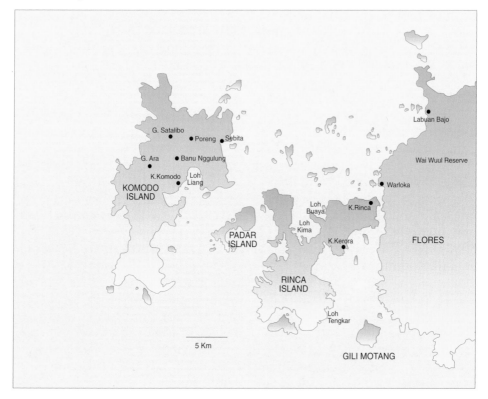

Transportation Details

	Hours	1996 cost	Distance (km)	Mode of transport
Labuan Bajo –Komodo	3–4	Rp.4,000 + 1,500	47	Ferry
Sape– Komodo	6–7	Rp.10,000 + 1,500	94	Ferry
Bima–Sape	1.5–2	Varies	65	Bus or hired car/minibus

No prebooking of tickets is required.

'taking only photos, leaving only footprints'. Villagers have had to forgo the use of their land and forest products due to the declaration of Komodo National Park. In return, so the theory goes, they will gain financially from tourism. Many tourists, however, visit by tour boat, bringing all the food and drink they need. The money they pay for the trip goes to Sumbawa, Bali or farther afield. The money paid for park entrance and rangers remains with the government to pay for anti-poaching patrols, ranger salaries, etc. Hiring local boats and buying locally is one of the few ways of directly supporting the people living adjacent to or within the park.

Currently most of the villagers derive their income from fishing within the park. As the park's marine management tightens they may revert to their earlier lifestyle, taking from the park, if they do not benefit economically from tourism.

Do It Yourself

Getting There
The two airports closest to the park are Bima, Sumbawa, and Labuan Bajo, Flores. Two government-run ferries ply daily, linking Sape, a short drive from Bima, and Labuan Bajo, stopping midway at Loh Liang, Komodo Island. The schedule is erratic, however, and one or occasionally both ferries may be out of action due to repairs. The bay at Loh Liang is too shallow for the government ferry to land, so a local boat meets it and takes passengers to the village and ranger station for a small additional charge.

Most tourists enter from Bima as it has more frequent and reliable flights, even though it requires a drive to Sape. The servicing of Labuan Bajo Airport is being improved to encourage more tourists to use it. The town is small and pretty, reasonably well serviced with hotels and small homestays called *losmen*, and its location makes it easy to visit different parts of the park.

Both Sape and Labuan Bajo have information centres for Komodo National Park, which are worth visiting as they should be able to give details on transportation, accommodation, food, water, communication, recreational activities, wildlife viewing and safety.

Visiting Komodo Island

There is accommodation for about 40 people at Loh Liang on a first come, first served basis. Rooms cost Rp.10,000 a night single, Rp.15,000 a night double. Recently renovated rooms, some with their own bathrooms, cost Rp.25,000 a night (1996 rates).

There are no private cooking facilities, but there is a cafeteria run by the Koperasi Komodo, which serves simple but adequate food. The information centre is worth a quick browse. It has part of a Komodo skeleton and dried eggs, as well as information on the park and samples of rocks, corals and snakes found on the island. No accommodation is available in Kampung Komodo.

Visiting Rinca Island

Rinca is not serviced by ferry, but as it is only two hours by local boat from Labuan Bajo it is becoming increasingly popular as a day destination. Longer tours can also be organised to this less visited but scenic island. Alternatively, a local boat can be chartered from Kampung Komodo. Visitors can try Pak Ali of Wisata Tours or charter the Loh Liang ranger station speedboat. The ranger station at Loh Buaya has 12 beds costing Rp.5,000 a night. Visitors need to bring their own food, and basic cooking facilities are provided. Water is available but needs to be boiled before drinking.

Labuan Bajo is a sleepy but scenic fishing village only two hours away from Rinca.

Details of Walking Tracks on Komodo and Rinca

Location	Track name	Distance (km)	Round trip (hours)	Comments
Komodo Island	Loh Liang– Banu Nggulung	5	1.5	Leads to old feeding station; flat, sandy & walked by most visitors
	Par-nuncep	2	0.5	Name means sunrise-sunset; track has viewing platform with wonderful views.
	Loh Liang –Gunung Ara (510 m)	13	6	Beautiful scenery; winds through different vegetation zones.
	Loh Liang– Poreng	9	3–4	Leads to memorial for Swiss baron; stunning scenery
	Loh Liang– Poreng– Sebita	10	6 (one way)	As above; boat must be organised in advance for pickup at Sebita.
	Loh Liang– Gunung Satalibo	Long; several paths	Overnight	Visitors must bring tents & gear; many animals & beautiful scenery
Rinca	Loop from Loh Buaya	5	1.5–2	Good views & wildlife; can see wild horses, cacti & monkeys, not present on Komodo
	Loh Buaya– Kampung Rinca	9	3–4 (one way)	Interesting walk to village
	Loh Buaya– Golo Kode	About 11	4	Triangular walk; good scenery

Additional Costs

Any person entering the park must pay an entrance fee of Rp.2,000, which is for a seven-day period. This is extremely low and does not come close to covering the cost of park protection. It is soon to be increased significantly (possibly to Rp.10,000), but this has not yet been officially announced. Even this will not cover the park's operating costs. There is an additional charge for rangers. Different-sized parties and lengths of walk incur varying costs, but to give readers an idea, the group fee for five people to walk to Banu Nggulung is Rp.2,500.

Cruise ships provide a comfortable and convenient way of visiting Komodo National Park.

Walks

Visitors are requested never to walk in the park without a ranger. While the Komodo dragons around the station are habituated to man, they are still dangerous and unpredictable, as are wild Komodos. Advice on the best walks for bird watching, animal spotting or general scenery is available from the ranger stations and information sites at Sape and Labuan Bajo.

Tours and Cruise Ships

A number of companies run tours specifically to Komodo National Park, while others include it on a longer trip through Nusa Tenggara. Boats can be chartered for those wishing to do it their own way.

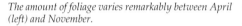
The amount of foliage varies remarkably between April (left) and November.

Some internationally based companies also include Komodo on their worldwide itineraries on an ad hoc basis, but due to the intermittent nature of the visits these are not discussed here. Listed instead are the major companies that have Komodo National Park as their primary tour destination.

One of the most popular is the Bali Sea Dancer cruise. Visitors may choose between a three- and four-night return trip from Bali to the park. Plush and well run, this is the easiest, quickest and by far most comfortable way to see Komodo dragons. Managed by the long-established Bali-based company Spice Island Cruises (address below), each trip allows time to walk to Banu Nggulung and snorkel or scuba dive at Pantai Merah. The trips also offer day excursions to Lombok and/or Sumbawa. Prices start at US$450 (1996 price).

There are a number of local, well-run companies offering trips to Komodo National Park. As the actual ships and itinerary of many vary from year to year, it is best to purchase a package from a travel agent. One of the more established companies is Parewa Tours and Travel (address below). Based in Bima, the company offers a good choice of trips. Some concentrate on the Komodo National Park area, but others include extensions to cultural centres on Flores and/or Sumba. This company has been operating for over 10 years and owns a series of traditional 20–25 m wooden boats equipped with powerful engines especially for the fast currents around Komodo. Parewa also owns a hotel in Bima, organises special charters and caters for scuba divers with advance notice. Prices vary depending on the number of people, but a three-day trip with about 10 people costs approximately US$200 per person (1996 price, ex Bima).

Choices for diving tours are more limited. Grand Komodo Tours and Travel (address below) has its main office in Bali, and it has smaller offices in Bima, Mataram and Maumere. Established in 1987, the company has two ships (Komodo Plus I and II), and trips can be booked by individuals or the whole ship (maximum eight divers) can be chartered. Trips are well run as the captain and crew are very familiar with the islands and dive sites. These boats also run regular trips from Sape to Komodo for general tourists if not booked by divers. A three-day cruise to Komodo (no diving) costs approximately US$290 per person (1996 price, ex Bima). Special dive charters around Komodo are also organised on these ships by other dive operators, such as Dive Trek East.

Sea Contacts (address below), which operates from Bali, is a new operation with the only facilities for oxygen-enriched safe air (Nitrox) in the region. The company's boats also have a qualified PADI and ANDI dive instructor on board to teach Nitrox diving or other scuba courses.

Choosing the Time of Year to Visit

The park and its scenery change dramatically depending on the time of year. The wet season runs from late December to March/April. Plants and animals burst into activity, keen to reproduce during this time of abundance. Flowers and insects abound and birds are busy nesting, but the rains make walking less enjoyable. The chance of seeing wild Komodo dragons is diminished, as they dislike the cooler temperatures that the rain brings. However, they can be seen all year round near the ranger station and old feeding area.

The prettiest time is just after the rains stop in April/May. Plants are still flowering, and the grasses that cover so much of the island are lush and green. Young Komodo dragons are hatching, although chances of

Even late in the dry season there is interesting vegetation, such as the distinctive red pods of the Sterculia foetida.

spotting one are slim. The only drawback is that the lush vegetation means birds and animals are harder to spot.

By June/July the daytime temperature starts rising, grasses start turning brown and leaves begin to wilt and drop. Life is still abundant and a few late flowers remain, but as the vegetation starts decreasing, animals collect around the water holes and are easier to spot. Male Komodo dragons fight for access to females, making an impressive sight as they rear up on their hind legs. July/August is peak tourist season as it coincides with the northern hemisphere summer break. The park gets over 200 visitors daily, and accommodation becomes hard to get.

Rules are strict within Komodo National Park, to ensure visitor safety and for the preservation of the park.

By October/November the grasses have turned honey brown, many trees have lost their leaves and the ground is dry and dusty. Yet it is still a good time for visitors, as animals are increasingly drawn to freshwater sites. Just before the first rains, many plants are already throwing out fresh leaves and, in the case of the kapuk hutan tree, huge bright red flowers. With other food still scarce, these act like magnets for birds in the region.

Diving

Scuba diving can be organised through the ranger station at Loh Liang. This facility opened in mid-1996, and several of the rangers have become certified divers. The cost is US$75 per person (1996 price). Most other diving is done from live-aboard boats, but from Labuan Bajo (ask for Pak Condo) day trips can

be taken into the park area. There are many projects under way, and new facilities and boats should soon be available. For more information on diving, see "The Underwater World" (page 61).

What to Take

Visitors to Indonesia should check with their doctor to ensure that they are vaccinated against endemic diseases, have appropriate medicine and are in good physical shape. They should take out medical insurance, as the cost of evacuation from remote areas is high (and local treatment facilities minimal) in the Komodo region. Little in the way of essentials can be bought, so visitors should bring everything they need, as well as any extra items, such as fruit, vegetables, snacks. On each walk they must take along plenty of fresh water, a sun hat and binoculars. Sunscreen and insect repellent should be applied. Those visiting Komodo Island for just a day trip to walk to Banu Nggulung are relatively close to help and are trekking on a well-worn trail. However, those planning to stay longer or wishing to do other treks should have loose cotton long pants and a long-sleeved shirt, sturdy walking shoes and a first aid kit. The walks are hot and tough, and once off the beaten path visitors are likely to come across snakes and other potentially threatening creatures on the island.

All Visitors

Visitors to the park are requested to observe the basic rules—do not take anything, do not litter, try to take your garbage back off the island with you, conserve water, be careful with fires (smoking is not allowed on the trails) and always observe basic safety rules. As in other wild areas, the golden rule is never to underestimate the dangers. People become used to seeing the 'tame' Komodos close to the ranger station, but there is no such thing as a tame Komodo!

Contacts

Spice Island Cruises
P.O. Box 3581
Denpasar, Bali 80228
Tel.: 62-361-286283
Fax: 62-361-286284
E-mail: balicruz@rad.net.id
Web site: http://www.indo.com/cruises/spice_island/index.html

Parewa Tours and Travel
Jl. Sumbawa no. 19
Bima, NTB
Tel.: 62-374-44221
Fax: 62-374-43440

Grand Komodo Tours and Travel
Jl. Hang Tuah no. 26,
P.O. Box 3477
Denpasar, Bali 80034
Tel.: 62-361-287166
Fax: 62-361-287165
E-mail: gkomodot@dps.mega.net.id

Sea Contacts
Danny Charlton
Jl. By Pass Ngurah Rai 2AB
Suwung, Denpasar, Bali
Tel.: 62-361-721979
Fax: 62-361-721976
E-mail: seacontacts@indo.com
Web site: http://www.indo.com/diving/seacontacts

Attacks on Humans

Attacks by Komodo dragons on humans should be one of the easiest areas to research, but it is actually the hardest. Until recently the region had only an oral history, and time has faded memories. Officials do not want to advertise past misfortunes and scare away valuable tourists. Others tell stories because they think people want to hear them. The author has tried to include only verified accounts or those that appear widely accepted.

Two deaths have occurred recently. The grave of a Swiss baron

Opposite: At Banu Nggulung a fenced-in area keeps visitors inside and Komodo dragons free to range outside.

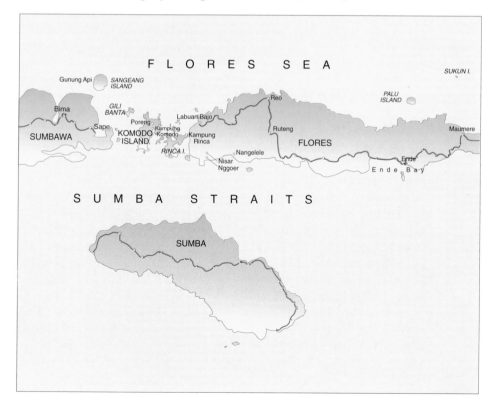

stands high in the hills at Poreng; his story follows. The second death was that of a young child on Rinca.

Other villagers have been bitten but, thanks to modern medicine, survived. Scientists, rangers and zookeepers have all received small bites and wounds during their work with the animals. These heal slowly and require antibiotic treatment to avoid severe infection and death. The most serious bites within the park in recent years have been on Rinca, reinforcing the local belief that the indigenous people of Kampung Komodo are not attacked by Komodos as they are kin. Interestingly, before the early 1970s, when Auffenberg visited, there were no known attacks on Rinca.

The following list of attacks has been compiled from the author's years of travelling in the region and talking to people, combined with information from Auffenberg (the first six attacks).

1931– A Komodo Island teenager bled to death after a Komodo attack. Three people were cutting wood in a clearing when the animal attacked.

1947– "A policeman from Flores was bitten in 1947 while petting a 2m *ora* (Komodo dragon) that was completely tied. The *ora* apparently lunged upward and tore out the man's right biceps. The villagers heard he died one week later in the Ruteng hospital from a severe infection." (Auffenberg, 1981).

1956– Hunters from Sumbawa who left a sick member of their group on Komodo returned the next day to find parts of the body eaten.

1957– A villager from Nisar, on the southwest coast of Flores near Nangelele, was attacked and eaten.

??– In southwest Flores, at Nggoer village, a large Komodo entered a man's garden and chased his chickens. The man chased the Komodo, which turned around and bit him below the calf. The man survived.

??– Another villager from Nggoer was attacked while cutting grass. He did not hear the Komodo dragon approach and was bitten on the leg. He remained sickly for two years, then died.

1974– Baron Rudolph von Reding was eaten.

1985– A Rinca woman was bitten on the leg but survived.

1987?–A six-year-old boy from Rinca was killed. He was attacked by a Komodo after descending the steps of a house. People chased away the animal, but the boy died from wounds to the stomach and chest. A gory photograph of his remains can be seen in an album at the park office. The Komodo dragon was trapped and taken to Wai Wuul, where it was released, although it is said to have returned to Rinca.

1989– A Flores farmer was attacked but survived.

1996– A teacher was jogging around the outside of a school playground at Rinca when a Komodo dragon ambushed him and bit him on the leg. The man jumped the fence into the playground to get away. Other villagers heard his screams and beat off the animal.

More tales exist, but many are derived from the above incidents. Having been passed from person to person, the dates or locations in the stories may have been changed. There is a story of another foreign tourist, probably French, being eaten in the mid-1980s. In one version, the person was bitten and died years later from recurring problems with the infections.

Interestingly, the majority of Komodo dragons do not attack humans; instead, they run away or completely ignore people. As many scientists can verify, most animals do not attack unless cornered. It appears to be rogue animals, those that have lost their fear of man, that cause the problems. This may explain why a series of attacks often occurs at one location.

The Legend of Baron Rudolph von Reding

By far the most famous tale of a Komodo dragon eating a man is

The inscription on Baron Rudolph von Reding's memorial cross reads, "He loved nature throughout his life."

The baron's memorial cross is at Poreng, a spectacular location about two hours' walk from Loh Liang.

that of the Swiss baron who disappeared on the island in 1974.

A tour of the Indonesian archipelago was organised by Kuoni, one of Switzerland's leading tour companies. To make it more attractive, the company had arranged for a top guide to accompany the group, as well as a professor of zoology who had spent time studying rhinos in Sumatra and was considered an expert on Indonesian wildlife.

Baron Rudolph von Reding was a sporty man who had represented his country as ambassador to various European nations. He loved travelling, but his less adventurous wife preferred to remain at their castle in Switzerland. He and 10 or so others set out to visit Java, Sumatra, Sulawesi and Bali before the highlight of the trip, the rarely visited Komodo Island. But after nearly a month together, the adventurers were beginning to annoy one another. The baron was 84 years old and used to getting his own way. He did not always want to accompany the other travellers, and tensions were building.

Komodo Island was a nature reserve but not yet a national park. The group got their permits at Labuan Bajo in Flores, came across by fishing boat and landed on a beach a few kilometres north of the current landing site at Loh Liang Bay. There were no tourist trails. Wandering along the beach, the visitors spotted wild Komodos and fed them on goat. After they had walked several kilometres, they settled down to eat the lunch they

106

had brought. But the baron, sick of his company and fed up with the food, decided to go back to the boat.

The group refused to follow the baron, so the tour leader stayed with them while the baron left alone. It did not seem a bad idea—the baron would follow the shoreline back the way they had come. While the Komodos were known to be carnivorous, no one, not even the professor of zoology, had any idea that they might kill and eat a human being. The Europeans knew of no record of this occurring.

Determined to enjoy the experience they had travelled so far for, the group paused for a few hours, swimming in the cool sea, eating lunch and having a leisurely rest, before strolling back to the boat. On their return, the baron was nowhere to be seen. They had not passed him, and the crew had not seen him. It was now late afternoon, and despite searching, they found no trace of him.

The transport from Flores was a small, old wooden fishing boat, and the Europeans had little faith in the crew's ability to sail back through the treacherous waters at night. Since they had anticipated only a day trip, they had virtually finished their supply of drinking water and food. With the sun fast disappearing, the guide had little choice but to get the rest of his group to safety on Flores and send over a search party the next day. Water and food were left for the baron in case he returned to the boat's mooring point.

About a hundred searchers returned the next day, but all that turned up were the baron's glasses and part of his camera, high in the hills behind the beach. Had he wandered inland for shade and lost his way? Had he walked up the hill to get his bearings or take some scenic photos? Had the baron fainted, had a stroke, stopped for a nap or fallen and twisted his ankle, only to be eaten by the Komodo, or had he put up a futile fight against the 10-foot beast? No one will ever know. His body was not found.

Stunned, the group returned to Switzerland, where they encountered a disbelieving audience. The baron's estate was suspended and his wife left destitute, unable to inherit until the matter was settled. After several years, despite the odd circumstances, Baron von Reding was officially declared dead, eaten by one or more Komodo dragons.

All those involved in the incident were left with scars. The zoology professor never joined another expedition and refuses to discuss the topic. The tour company and operator, quite rightly, were proved not to have been negligent, but it was many years before they returned to Komodo waters. The baron's widow insists her husband died with a Catholic priest at his side!

The ramifications of the event are more far reaching than just the direct effects it had. The incident created a legend. Every visitor to the park hears the story. The burden of it is carried by all rangers and tour operators today, who are acutely aware that it could happen again, to any one of them, if they do not keep a close eye on their group.

Glossary

ANDI: American Nitrox Divers International

cloaca: The vent in reptiles and birds where the intestinal and urinary ducts end

cloacal rosettes: Two small rosettes of scales near the vent, usually surrounding a small depression. These are thought to be present only on males and hence form a method of sexing Komodo dragons.

cold-blooded: A general term used for animals whose body temperature fluctuates with the surrounding environment. However, some animals, such as the Komodo dragon, are able to use stored energy to raise their body temperature higher than the surroundings at times.

dynamite fishing: This term is commonly used in Indonesia, although dynamite is rarely used. The explosion is often created by a fertiliser mixture.

ecosystem: A single community of organisms and their environment

ectoparisitic: Relating to external parasites

enteritis: Inflammation of the intestines, particularly the small intestines

enzymatic action: Regulation of the rate of biochemical reactions by enzymes, which are protein catalysts

genera: A taxonomic term; plural for genus

habituated animals: Animals used to the presence of man but not tame

hemi-penes: Paired male copulatory organs found in certain reptiles

herbaceous: Referring to vegetation composed of tall herbs that die down for part of the year and survive underground

marsupials: Animals whose young are born in a very early stage of development and are then usually carried in the pouch of the mother as they develop; common in Australia.

opportunistic: Referring to a feeding strategy used by certain animals that consume virtually any suitable food item, dead or alive, that they come across alive, that they come across

pheromone: A chemical substance secreted by an animal, which alters the behaviour of others of the same species

PHPA: Perlindungan Hutan dan Pelestrian Alam, Protection of Forest and Conservation of Nature. This is Indonesia's national park authority and is part of the Ministry of Forestry.

TNC: The Nature Conservancy, an environmental group working on an underwater program at Komodo National Park

zooxanthellae: Single-cell algae that live symbiotically within the cells of some marine animals, such as most reef forming corals, giant clams and some anemones and hydroids

Bibliography

Adams, M. and Carwardine, M. 1990. *Last Chance to See*. New York: Serious Productions.

Attenborough, D. 1957. *Zoo Quest for a Dragon*. Oxford University Press.

Auffenberg, W. 1981. *The Behavioral Ecology of the Komodo Monitor.* Gainesville: University of Florida.

Auffenberg, W. 1980. *The Herpetofauna of Komodo, with notes on adjacent areas.* Bulletin of the Florida State Museum Biological Sciences, Vol. 25, no. 2. Gainesville: University of Florida.

Barnes, R.H., Hembree, E.D. and Silalahi, S. Aug. 1990. *Observations and Research on the Cetacean Fishery of Lembata, Indonesia.* WWF.

Blower et al. Oct. 1977. *Proposed Komodo National Park Management Plan 1978–82.* Bogor: FAO Field Report 3.

Broughton, M. 1936. *A Modern Dragon Hunt on Komodo.* National Geographic, 70:321–31.

Burden, D. 1927. *Stalking the Dragon Lizard on the Island of Komodo.* National Geographic, 52 (2): 216-33.

Cesar, H. July 1996. *The Economic Value of Indonesian Coral Reefs.* The World Bank.

Ciofi, C. Nov. 1994. *Conservation Genetics of the Komodo Dragon, Report 1.* Field Work, The Durrell Institute of Conservation and Ecology, The Institute of Zoology and Universitas Gadjah Madah.

Diamond, J. Dec. 1992. *The Evolution of Dragons in the Jungles of Indonesia.* Discover.

Forth, G. 1988. *Komodo as Seen from Sumba: Comparative Remarks on an Eastern Indonesian Relationship Terminology.* Bijdragen, Tot de Taal, land en Volkenkunde.

Hecht, M.K. 1975. *The Morphology and Relationships of the Largest Known Terrestrial Lizard, Megalania prisca Owen, from the Pleistocene of Australia.* Proc. Royal Soc. Of Victoria, 87:239–24.

Holthus, P. Oct. 1994. *Coastal and Marine Environment of Komodo National Park: Reconnaissance Assessment.* The Nature Conservancy.

Jones, D., Dekker, R. and Roselaar, C. 1995. *The Megapodes*. UK: Oxford University Press.

Karjon, Rafael Yosif. 1991. *Pengelolaan Hutan dan Pelestarian Satwa Komodo di Pulau Komodo*. Denpasar: Universitas Udayana Fakultas Sastra.

King, D. and Green, B. 1993. *Goanna–The Biology of the Varanid Lizards*. UNSW Press Australian Natural History Series.

Kvalvagnaes, K. and Halim, M. Aug. 1979. *Report on a Survey of Marine Areas of the Proposed Komodo National Park*. Bogor: FAO Field Report 4.

Lilley, R. 1994. *A Feasibility Study on the In-Situ Captive Breeding of Komodo Dragons on Padar Island, Komodo National Park*. UK: Durrell Institute of Conservation Ecology, University of Kent.

Lutz, D. and Lutz, J. 1991. *Komodo, the Living Dragon*. Dimi Press.

Needham, R. 1986. *Principles and Variations in the Social Classification of Komodo*. Bijdragen, Tot de Taal, land en Volkenkunde.

Pet, J. and Djohani, R. 1996. *A Framework for Management of the Marine Resources of Komodo National Park and Surrounding Fishing Grounds in Eastern Indonesia*. The Nature Conservancy.

Quammen, D. 1996. *The Song of the Dodo, Island Biogeography in an Age of Extinctions*. USA: Scribner.

Rich, T. and Hall, B. 1979. *Rebuilding a Giant Lizard: Megalania prisca*. Aust. Nat. Hist.,19:310–3.

Sunquist, F. Nov. 1995. *The Lizard Kings, Komodo Dragons*. National Geographic World.

Tomascik, T., Mah, A.J., Nontji, A. and Moosa, M.K. 1997. *The Ecology of the Indonesian Seas*. Periplus.

2–4 April, 1996. *Workshop on Sustainable Tourism and Biodiversity, Komodo National Park, Labuan Bajo*. The Durrell Institute of Conservation and Ecology, The Wallace Development Institute and The Komodo National Park.

1995. *Komodo Monitor, Population and Habitat Viability Assessment (PHVA) Workshop*. Dec. 4–7, 1995. Taman Safari, Indonesia, Cisuara, Indonesia.

Verheijen, J. 1982. *Komodo Het Eiland, Het Volk En De Taal.* The Hague, Martinus Nijhoff.

Vickers-Rich, P. and Hewitt Rich, T. 1993. *Wildlife of Gondwana.* NSW, Australia: Reed.

Viloteau, N. 1992. *Les dragons de Komodo.* France: Les Editions Arthaud.

Walsh, T., Rosscoe, R. and Birchard, G. *Dragon Tales, The History, Husbandry, and Breeding of Komodo Monitors at the National Zoological Park.* The Vivarium, Vol. 4:6.

Index

feeding, digestion 26, 30–33, 41, 83, 90–91
genetics 15, 17, 23, 28, 29, 36, 83, 87
hearing 24, 34–36
home range 28–29, 83
interactions 29–30
life cycle 39–41
life span 41, 83, 87
population, distribution 11, 17, 19, 26–28, 81, 83
protection 20–21, 87
saliva 24, 31, 32
sex determination 38–39, 83
size 24, 25
smell 24, 32, 33–34, 37
speed 24–25
swimming 17, 25, 26, 28
thermoregulation 26, 36, 87–88
threats 21, 41, 82
vision 24
Komodo Island 8–9, 11, 12–13, 15, 16, 17, 19, 20, 23, 24, 25, 27, 28, 36, 45, 52, 63, 64, 66, 67, 71–79, 83, 84, 93–101, 103, 104, 106

L
Labuan Bajo 11, 13, 15, 20, 23, 28, 64, 67, 79, 93, 94, 95, 97, 100, 103, 106
lizards 7, 19, 24, 25, 26, 31, 32, 36, 39, 41, 55
Loh Liang 13, 36, 76, 93, 94, 95, 96, 100, 106
Loligo sp. 67
Lumnitzera sp. 50

M
Macaca fascicularis 53
mangrove 48, 50, 53, 55, 62, 64, 67, 82
Mbeliling and Nggorang 12, 15, 21
Megalania prisca 25, 26
megapode bird 57, 83
Megapodius freycinet 57
Megapodius reinwardt reinwardt 57
Moluccas 18
monitor lizard 7, 19, 25, 26

monkeys 14, 45, 49, 50, 52, 53, 96
monsoon forest 48, 49–50, 52, 53, 82

N
Nephila sp. 59
Nusa Kode 15, 27

O
Opuntia nigricans 49

P
Padar 11, 12, 13, 17, 20, 23, 27, 28, 50, 52, 55, 57, 63, 93
Pandanus-spinifex 50
Paradoxurus hermaphroditus 55
pigs 12, 30, 32, 40, 41, 45, 49, 50, 52, 57, 63
Pteropus sp. 53

Q
quasi-cloud forest 48, 50

R
rain forest 16, 43
rangers 27, 28, 38, 63, 71, 76, 77, 78, 79, 82, 84, 94, 97, 100, 104, 107
Rattus rintjanus 55
Rhincodon typus 63
Rhizophora sp. 50
Rinca 11, 12, 13, 14, 15, 16, 17, 20, 23, 25, 27, 28, 44, 49, 50, 52, 53, 55, 64, 68, 76, 78, 83, 93, 95, 96, 103, 104, 105
rodents 32, 41, 52, 55, 57

S
Sape 27, 73, 76, 94, 97, 99
savannah 16, 26, 43, 48, 49, 50, 51, 52, 59
Schleichera oleosa 50
snakes 25, 32, 33, 39, 40, 41, 55, 63, 95, 101
spiders 59
Sterculia foetida 99
Sterculia sp. 50
Sumba 8–9, 11, 72, 73, 74, 98, 103

Acknowledgements

My greatest thanks go to Ron Lilley, WWF Jakarta, without whose encouragement, support and constructive criticism this book would never have been started and certainly never have been completed. His photos have also improved the pictorial content.

My curiosity and love of the islands have come from the hundreds of sweat-stained hours spent trekking around Komodo National Park with various rangers over the last eight years. My great thanks to them for their companionship and the wealth of local knowledge they shared with me; and to Pak Bambang Sugiarto, the local harbourmaster, and the villagers of Kampung Komodo—particularly Pak Ishaka Mansour and Pak Ali—with whom I talked, travelled and shared sweet tea.

I would also like to acknowledge the help and support received from numerous staff of PHPA, including Pak Bambang Hartono, the head of Taman Nasional Komodo, Labuan Bajo.

Many others contributed to the content and accuracy of the text, including Carol Bach, Registrar, Taronga Zoo, Australia; Dr. Clive Burrett, Geology Department, University of Tasmania; Claudio Ciofi, Zoological Society of London; Dr. Harold Goodwin, Durrell Institute of Conservation and Ecology, Kent, UK; Jiri Holba, Taman Safari Indonesia; Paul Jepson, Birdlife, Bogor; Dr. Francis Lim, Singapore Zoological Gardens; Dr. Tom Reidarson, San Diego SeaWorld; Ir Putra Sastrawan, Udayana University, Bali; Pak Sutarmin, Pak Malik and Dr. Bambang of Ragunan Zoo, Jakarta; and Trooper Walsh, National Zoological Park, Washington, DC.

Specifically for assistance on the underwater chapter, thanks to Rili Djohani, Pak Condo, Dr. Jos Pet, and Herling Sanger from The Nature Conservancy, Indonesia; and to Dr. Tomas and Anmarie Tomascik. Thanks also to the library staff at WWF Jakarta; Dr. Charlotte Peter for sharing her knowledge of the details surrounding the death of Baron von Reding; Dr. Michael Hitchcock for his clarification of the history of the Sultanate of Bima; and Dr. Jonathan Agranoff for his helpful comments relating to recent attacks by Komodo dragons on humans.

Where possible I have contacted the authors quoted; my thanks to them for both their initial research and their permission to reproduce it.

For reading various chapters of the book and making constructive suggestions, my appreciation goes to Suzanne Gendron, Brechje Jager, Andy Wight and my parents, David and Sybil Metcalfe. I would like to further thank Brechje for patiently translating Dutch texts, and my parents for regularly scouring libraries for obscure references. Thanks also to my husband, Anthony, for putting up with my many absences over the years and providing support through the compilation of the book.

Additional thanks to John Daniels, Spice Island Cruises, whose continuing belief in the beauty and uniqueness of the area has enabled me to visit regularly. Last, but far from least, my appreciation to the wonderful crews of MV Island Explorer and MV Spice Islander who first introduced me to the Komodo region and Nusa Tenggara and then, on and off, for seven years shared many of my adventures and helped me understand the people, the places and the cultures far better.

Photo Credits

All photographs in this book are by Claire Ellis, with the exception of the following:

Anthony Ellis, pp. 14, 53, 60, 62, 63, 65 (top), 66, 86, 88, 90
Ron Lilley, pp. 39, 51, 54, 56, 59, 65 (bottom), 89, 102

Nature Series

Orchids of Asia
The definitive book for lovers of tropical orchids. A large and lavish award-winning book filled with notes on the various species of orchids found in Asia. There is also an interesting chapter on myths and aphrodisiacs.

An Underwater Guide to the South China Sea
An introduction to the wondrous marine life in the South China Sea, with over 200 exquisite colour photographs of anemones, sponges, corals, molluscs and fish.

Living Corals
Just as coconut palms are associated with the South Sea, corals and coral reefs are associated with the tropics. Starting with the basic facts, this book explains the complex biology of the *madrepores*, the builders of the coral reefs that encircle tropical islands and fringe tropical shores.

Kingfishers of the World
A comprehensive study of all 86 recognised species of kingfishers, with accompanying illustrations in full colour. Includes a section on how knowledge about kingfishers has grown over the years.

Hawaiian Insects and Their Kin
An exploration of the fascinating array of insect species on the Hawaiian Islands, ranging from those found in young caves by the ocean to those found on the cold, stone desert of active volcanoes.

Diving in Tahiti
A detailed guide to over 70 dive sites in the French Polynesian islands. Contains tips on weather conditions, first aid and how to identify marine life (both benign and dangerous).

Birds of Singapore
Dr. Christopher Hails covers all the major bird watching habitats in Singapore and explains how nature has adapted to urban encroachment. Illustrated to reflect with great accuracy the many species of birds found in Singapore.

Plants and Flowers of Malaysia
Malaysia has a rich variety of flowering plants. This book captures some of the wonderful, weird, beautiful, rare and common plants that are part of Malaysia's natural heritage.